Introduction

The Advantage Math Series for grades 3–6 offers instruction and practice for key skills in each math strand recommended by the National Council for Teachers of Mathematics (NCTM), including

- numeration and number theory
- operations
- geometry
- measurement
- patterns, functions, and algebra
- data analysis and probability
- problem solving

Take a look at all the advantages this math series offers . . .

teaching component

Strong Skill Instruction

- The **teaching component** at the top of the activity pages provides the support students need to work through the book independently.

- Plenty of **skill practice** pages will ensure students master essential math computation skills they need to increase their math fluency.

- A **problem-solving strand** is woven within skill practice pages to offer students an opportunity to practice critical thinking skills.

skill practice

problem solving

Introduction

- **Mixed-practice pages** include a variety of math concepts on one workbook page. This challenges students to think through each problem rather than rely on a predictable format.

Assessment

- The "Take a Test Drive" pages provide practice using a **test-taking** format such as those included in national standardized and proficiency tests.

- The **tracking sheet** provides a place to record the number of right answers scored on each activity page. Use this as a motivational tool for students to strive for 100% accuracy.

Answer Key

- Answers for each page are provided at the back of the books to make **checking answers quick and easy.**

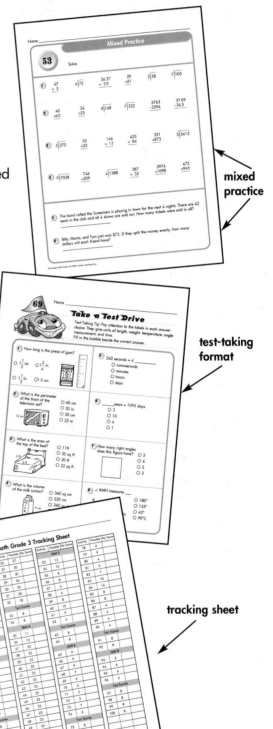

mixed
practice

test-taking
format

tracking sheet

Word Names and Standard Numerals

1

Millions			Thousands			Ones		
Hundreds	Tens	Ones	Hundreds	Tens	Ones	Hundreds	Tens	Ones
	2 ,	5	7	8 ,	2	7	2	

⭐ Use this chart to help you write and read large numbers. Large numbers are arranged into groups of 3 places separated by commas. This number is read as "two million, five hundred seventy-eight thousand, two hundred seventy-two."

Write these numbers in word form.

1 5,093,185 _____

2 7,431,050 _____

3 4,830,004 _____

⭐ A place value chart is also useful in reading and writing decimals. How do we read 3.041? This number is read as "three and forty-one thousandths."

Ones	Tenths	Hundredths	Thousandths
3 .	0	4	1

Write these decimals in word form.

4 0.023 _____

5 3.59 _____

6 2.607 _____

$2\frac{1}{5}$ is the same as two and one-fifth. Write these fractions in word form.

7 $4\frac{3}{8}$ _____

8 $2\frac{1}{6}$ _____

9 $\frac{12}{13}$ _____

Standard Form and Expanded Form

2

Millions			Thousands			Ones		
Hundreds	Tens	Ones	Hundreds	Tens	Ones	Hundreds	Tens	Ones
		8 ,	7	5	0 ,	3	0	0

★ 8,750,300 is a number expressed in **standard form**. In **expanded form**, this number is written as (8 x 1,000,000) + (7 x 100,000) + (5 x 10,000) + (3 x 100).

0.093 is read as "ninety-three thousandths." In **expanded form**, this decimal is written as (9 x 0.01) + (3 x 0.001).

Ones	Tenths 0.1	Hundredths 0.01	Thousandths 0.001
0 .	0	9	3

Write each number in expanded form.

1 2,305,467 _____

2 10.49 _____

3 5,413.2 _____

4 0.054 _____

Write each number in standard form.

5 7,000,000 + 80,000 + 5,000 + 600 + 20 + 9 _____

6 4,000 + 700 + 8 + 0.4 _____

7 8 thousand, fifty, and 9 hundredths _____

8 forty-seven thousandths _____

9 Write a decimal in standard and expanded form for a number that has a 2 in the tenths place, an 8 in the thousandths place, and a 6 in the hundredths place.

_____

Compare and Order

3

⭐ A number line can be used to compare decimals.

Since 95.73 is to the right of 95.57, you know that 95.73 is the higher number.

The Smith family home was on ⅔ of an acre of land, while the Gonzalez home was on ¾ of an acre of land. Which family had the larger property?

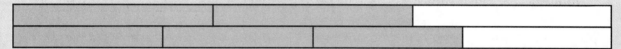

Looking at the fraction bar, you can see that ¾ is more than ⅔, so the Gonzalez family had a larger property than the Smith family.

Use the fraction bar to solve the problem.

1 Elephants use their trunks to lift heavy objects. One elephant might lift a log weighing ³⁄₁₀ of a ton. Another elephant could lift a rock weighing ⅕ of a ton. Does the log or the rock weigh more? Explain your answer.

_____

_____

_____

_____

Compare and Order

4

⭐ When comparing decimals, line up the decimal points, and look for the first place where the digits are different. If there are whole numbers, start to the left of the decimal point.

0.012 ◯ 0.014 Since the tenths and hundredths places are the same, compare the thousandths place. Since 4 is larger than 2, 0.012 < 0.014.

⭐ When comparing fractions, find the least common denominator of each fraction. Then compare the numerators. $\frac{2}{3}$ ◯ $\frac{1}{2}$ $\frac{2}{3} \times \frac{2}{2} = \frac{4}{6}$ $\frac{1}{2} \times \frac{3}{3} = \frac{3}{6}$ Since 4 is greater than 3, ⁴⁄₆ is greater than ³⁄₆. So, $\frac{2}{3} > \frac{1}{2}$

⭐ When you compare percents, follow the same steps as when you compare whole numbers. The larger the number, the greater the percent.

Order these numbers from least to greatest.

1 2.098, 3.089, 2.980, 2.908 _____

2 0.013, 0.301, 0.103, 0.031 _____

3 0.871, 0.187, 0.781, 0.817 _____

Use the symbols < and > to compare these fractions.

4 $\frac{3}{5}$ ◯ $\frac{4}{7}$ $\frac{4}{9}$ ◯ $\frac{3}{8}$ $\frac{2}{3}$ ◯ $\frac{3}{4}$

Circle the greater percent in each pair.

5 48% 84% 63% 36% 49% 92%

6 55% 45% 90% 99% 10% 100%

Name _____

5

 $\frac{1}{5} = 0.2$

To change the fraction to a decimal, divide the numerator (1) by the denominator (5).

$$5\overline{)1.0}^{\displaystyle 0.2}$$

To change 0.25 to a fraction, find the place value of the last digit. Since the 5 is in the hundredths place, 100 will be the denominator of the fraction.

$$0.25 = \frac{25}{100} = \frac{1}{4}$$

$$70\% = \frac{70}{100} = 0.70$$

As a fraction, 70% may be expressed as $\frac{70}{100}$.

As a decimal, 70% is expressed as 0.70.

Answer the questions.

1 Which of these is equivalent to ½? 0.6, ⅜, 0.5 _____

2 Which number is greater 0.75 or ⅘? _____

3 What fraction is equivalent to 0.80? _____

4 Which of these is not equivalent to ⅘? 80% or 0.08 _____

5 How can 50% be expressed as a decimal and as a fraction in lowest terms?
decimal _____   fraction _____

6 At the movie theater on Monday night, ¾ of the audience bought popcorn. On Tuesday night, 70% bought popcorn, and on Wednesday night 0.65 bought popcorn. If the size of the audience was the same each night, on which night was the most popcorn sold?

_____

Numbers and Equivalents

 6

Decimal	Fraction	Percent
0.25	¼	25%

1 About 20% of all immigrants came from Eastern Europe. Write this percent as a decimal and a fraction. _____ _____

2 Phil had completed 40% of his report. How much of his report did Phil still need to complete? Express this as a percent, a decimal, and a fraction.

_____ _____ _____

3 Order these regions from least to greatest.

_____

_____

_____

_____

_____

Area	Part of Total
Northwestern Europe	20%
Central Europe	0.30
Southern Europe	¼
Eastern Europe	0.20
Other Countries	⁵⁄₁₀₀

4 Look at the grid. Write the part shaded as a
percent _____
decimal _____
fraction _____

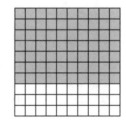

5 Complete this table.
Write each fraction in simplest terms.

Decimal	Fraction	Percent
0.60		
	⁶⁄₂₅	
		80%
0.06		
	³⁄₁₀	
		55%

Name _____

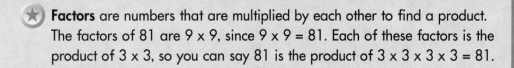

Exponents and Factors

7

⭐ **Factors** are numbers that are multiplied by each other to find a product. The factors of 81 are 9 x 9, since 9 x 9 = 81. Each of these factors is the product of 3 x 3, so you can say 81 is the product of 3 x 3 x 3 x 3 = 81.

3 x 3 x 3 x 3 = 81 is a **prime factorization**.

This prime factorization can be written using an exponent. An **exponent** shows how many times a number, known as a **base**, is used as a factor. Since 3 is multiplied by itself 4 times, you write:

> A prime number has only 1 and itself as factors.

$$81 = 3^4$$ This is read as "3 to the fourth power."

base

8^2 is read as "8 to the second power" or "8 squared."
9^3 is read as "9 to the third power" or "9 cubed."

Find the prime factorization of the following numbers.

1   24 _____   30 _____   40 _____

Write these numbers in standard form.

2 10^3 _____ 5^2 _____ 2^4 _____

---

3   There are about 4,000 different species of mammals. Using prime factorization, Tony wrote this number as 200 x 5 x 2^2. Write the proper prime factorization.

_____

4   Alice's grandmother's age is expressed as 7 x 3 x 2^2. How old is Alice's grandmother? _____

Name _____

Evaluating Expressions

8

⭐ Marcia was writing a report on the solar system. She found that the distance of Mars from the sun could be expressed as 57×2^2 million kilometers.

To find this distance, first look at the number with the exponent:
$2^2 = 2 \times 2 = 4$.
Next, multiply by 57: $57 \times 4 = 228$. Mars is 228 million kilometers from the sun.

Find the value of these expressions.

1 $3 \times 8^2 =$ $2^3 \times 6 =$ $5 \times 3^3 =$

2 $6 \times 2^4 =$ $82 \times 3^2 =$ $53 \times 2^5 =$

Evaluate these expressions.

3 $b - 20$, for $b = 61$ $(m - 12) + 5$, for $m = 23$

4 $8 \times (n + 2)$, for $n = 5$ $25 - (21 - g)$, for $g = 18.5$

Evaluate the expression $c/5$ for each value of c.

5 $c = 15$ $c = 30$

   $c = 80$ $c = 52$

---

6 Nancy traveled m miles 3 separate times to go to the library. How far did she travel if $m = 5$ miles?

_____

Take a Test Drive

Fill in the bubble beside the correct answer.

1 What is 0.60 as a fraction in simplest terms?
- ○ $\frac{3}{50}$
- ○ $\frac{3}{5}$
- ○ $\frac{1}{6}$
- ○ $\frac{1}{10}$

2 What is the value of 9×3^2?
- ○ 100
- ○ 90
- ○ 81
- ○ 93

3 What is $\frac{6}{25}$ expressed as a percent?
- ○ 16%
- ○ 24%
- ○ 6%
- ○ 20%

4 What is two million, sixty-seven thousand, eight hundred one in standard form?
- ○ 2,670,801
- ○ 2,067,801
- ○ 2,067,810
- ○ 2,670,810

5 Which number is equivalent to $\frac{3}{4}$?
- ○ 34%
- ○ 0.75
- ○ 0.075
- ○ 50%

6 What is seventy-eight thousandths in standard form?
- ○ 0.0078
- ○ 0.780
- ○ 0.087
- ○ 0.078

7 What is 55% expressed as a fraction?
- ○ $\frac{1}{55}$
- ○ $\frac{11}{20}$
- ○ $\frac{16}{20}$
- ○ $\frac{1}{15}$

8 Which number is NOT equivalent to 80%?
- ○ 0.080
- ○ $\frac{4}{5}$
- ○ 0.80
- ○ $\frac{8}{10}$

Name _____

Take a Test Drive

Fill in the bubble beside the correct answer.

1 What is the value of
$18 - (6^2 \div 9) \times 3 - 2$?
- ○ 4
- ○ 3
- ○ 5
- ○ 6

2 What is 0.056 in word form?
- ○ five hundred sixty thousandths
- ○ fifty-six hundredths
- ○ fifty-six thousandths
- ○ fifty-six and five thousandths

3 A number cubed is 64. What is the number?
- ○ 3
- ○ 4
- ○ 5
- ○ 6

4 Which of the following is NOT equivalent to ²/₅?
- ○ 40%
- ○ 0.4
- ○ 4%
- ○ ⁴/₁₀

5 What is the prime factorization of 45?
- ○ 3 x 3 x 5
- ○ 5 x 5 x 3
- ○ 9 x 5
- ○ 3 x 3 x 3 x 5

6 How do we write twenty-one percent as a decimal?
- ○ 0.21
- ○ 0.021
- ○ 2.1
- ○ 210.00

7 Which numbers are in order from greatest to least?
- ○ 6.056 6.560 6.506
- ○ 6.560 6.506 6.056
- ○ 6.560 6.056 6.506
- ○ 6.506 6.056 6.560

8 What part of the grid is shaded?
- ○ ⁷/₂₀
- ○ 65%
- ○ ¹³/₂₀
- ○ 0.035

Name _____

11

⭐ Regroup 12 ten thousands as 1 hundred thousand and 2 ten thousands

Regroup 11 thousands as 1 ten thousand and 1 thousand

Regroup 11 million as 1 ten million and 1 million ⟶ 1 1 1 1 ⟵ Regroup 10 tens as 1 hundred

```
   1  1 1  1
  138,053,563
+ 143,368,343
  ───────────
  281,421,906
```

Add.

1)

```
   2,103        4,198,517     54,111,035           43        6,357
  71,957           96,454            590        7,087       12,003
+ 83,099               33             18          854           96
 ───────     +        491     +       439   + 1,236,781   +    432
```

2)

```
  5,987,034            8          754     3,429,623      83,736
     53,999           43        2,854     5,873,154      24,451
         87          679        2,460   +    34,962    +  3,598
+       624        1,688           34    ──────────    ────────
                + 48,321     +    873
```

The table below shows the attendance at some Major League baseball games. Use this table to answer the questions that follow.

3) What was the combined attendance of the Rockies, Orioles, and Indians games. _____

4) When Jeff added the attendance of the Royals and Cubs games he had a sum of 79,387. What was Jeff's mistake? Find the correct answer. _____
_____

5) What was the combined attendance of all five games?

_____

Home Team	Attendance
Rockies	45,397
Cubs	39,989
Orioles	34,239
Royals	40,408
Indians	23,576

Name _____

Subtracting Whole Numbers

12

Remember: If the top number is smaller than the bottom number, you need to regroup.

```
    1 12
  225,981,679
 − 55,440,227
  170,541,452
```

Subtract.

1

6,309,005	1,563,615	81,506	560,531	8,589,214
− 977,368	− 8,727	−32,960	− 2,385	− 572,193

2

65,145,008	6,982,431	34,257	8,692,163	83,520
−53,876,469	− 35,487	− 4,983	− 49,638	− 3,719

Find the missing digits.

3

▢,9▢5	▢7,▢0▢	1,8▢2,39▢	8,▢29,214	83,▢50
−1,▢7▢	−3▢,3▢5	− 10,4▢2	− 57▢,12▢	−▢▢,2▢9
1,389	10,818	1,851,921	7,657,085	80,441

The table below shows some of the highest mountains in the world. Use this table to answer the questions that follow.

4 How much higher is Mount Everest than Kamet?

_____

5 Is there a greater difference between Cho Oyu and Nanga Parbat or Nanga Parbat and Nanda Devi?

_____

Mountain	Country	Elevation
Everest	China/Nepal	29,029 feet
Cho Oyu	China/Nepal	27,776 feet
Nanga Parbat	Pakistan	26,657 feet
Nanda Devi	India	25,643 feet
Kamet	China/India	25,446 feet

Name _____

Adding Decimals

13

⭐ Adding numbers with decimals is the same as adding whole numbers. Just make sure to line up the decimal points. You may add zeroes to make the numbers the same length.

```
  43.90
  62.04
+  9.70
───────
 115.64
```

Find the sum.

1

3.9	34.6	4.853	43.75	3.86
+2.7	+ 6.45	+4.56	+83.57	+24.52

2

4.896	12.89	364.3	300.54	64
+7.632	+31.76	+ 92.1	+ 89.3	+ 5.726

3

98.322	65.007	542.89	9,375	7,428,906.699
6.003	3.8	33.7	88.417	384,155.07
+483.7	37	524.98	3.008	7,489,601
	+ 9.35	+ 37.3	9,735	969
			84.871	+ 348,551.7
			+ 3.8	

Use this table to answer the questions that follow.

4 If these 4 golfers were on a golf team, what would their combined average be? _____

5 Is the combined average of Candie Kung and Karrie Webb higher than the combined average of Annika Sorenstam and Laura Diaz?

_____

Golfer's Name	Average Strokes Per Round
Annika Sorenstam	68.87
Karrie Webb	70.14
Laura Diaz	71
Candie Kung	71.2

Name _____

Subtracting Decimals

14

⭐ Subtracting numbers with decimals is the same as subtracting whole numbers. Just make sure to line up the decimal points. You may add zeroes to make the numbers the same length.

$$
\begin{array}{r}
516\ 410 \\
76\cancel{6}.\cancel{5}09 \\
-\ 39.245 \\
\hline
727.264
\end{array}
$$

Find the difference.

1

5.00	4.93	43.42	490.65	541.091
−3.62	−2.85	− 2.77	− 29.76	− 38.932

2

7.271	81.6	4,369.001	0.836	76,999.31
−3.68	−43.177	− 765.99	−0.248	− 56.37

3

89.715	15.78	5,912,736	472,879.3	87,546.88
−38.67	−12	− 58,345	− 76.05	−53,462.93

4 The normal temperature for a human is 98.6°F. If Jenna were sick and had a fever of 100.45°F, how far above normal was her temperature?

_____

5 Charlie spent $15.95 on school supplies and $3.50 for a hot dog and drink. He had $2.55 left when he got home. How much did he have at the start of the day?

_____

6 The area of New Hampshire is 9.351 thousand square miles, while the area of its neighbor Vermont is 9.614 thousand square miles. How much larger is Vermont than New Hampshire?

_____

Adding Fractions and Mixed Numbers

15 ⭐ $\frac{2}{7} + \frac{1}{6} = ?$ To add fractions that have different denominators, first find the least common multiple for each denominator and convert each fraction.

$$\frac{2}{7} = \frac{12}{42} \qquad \frac{1}{6} = \frac{7}{42}$$

Then, add the fractions with like denominators.

$$\frac{12}{42} + \frac{7}{42} = \frac{19}{42}$$

To add mixed numbers, first add the whole numbers, $12 + 5 = 17$, then add the fractions.

$$12\frac{5}{8} + 5\frac{7}{8} = ? \qquad \frac{5}{8} + \frac{7}{8} = \frac{12}{8}$$

Express the sum in simplest terms.

$$17\frac{12}{8} = 18\frac{4}{8} = 18\frac{1}{2}$$

Express the sum in simplest terms.

1 $\frac{1}{3} + \frac{1}{5} =$ $2\frac{1}{2} + 3\frac{1}{8} =$ $\frac{5}{6} + \frac{1}{3} =$

2 $3\frac{2}{3} + 2\frac{1}{7} =$ $\frac{3}{4} + \frac{5}{6} =$ $\frac{17}{20} + \frac{3}{20} =$

3 $5\frac{1}{5} + 3\frac{1}{4} =$ $\frac{1}{2} + \frac{1}{6} =$ $5\frac{8}{10} + 6\frac{3}{4} =$

4 $\frac{2}{3} + \frac{4}{5} + \frac{9}{10} =$ $6\frac{7}{8} + 3\frac{1}{5} + 4\frac{2}{3} =$

Subtracting Fractions and Mixed Numbers

16

★ $5\frac{1}{8} = \frac{41}{8}$
$-3\frac{5}{8} = \frac{29}{8}$
$\frac{12}{8} = 1\frac{4}{8} = 1\frac{1}{2}$

Express the difference in simplest terms.

1

$4\frac{1}{3}$
$-2\frac{2}{3}$

$\frac{4}{5}$
$-\frac{2}{3}$

$6\frac{3}{4}$
$-2\frac{1}{5}$

2

$9\frac{7}{8}$
$-6\frac{5}{8}$

$8\frac{4}{9}$
$-2\frac{7}{9}$

$\frac{5}{8}$
$-\frac{5}{16}$

3

$\frac{8}{9}$
$-\frac{3}{8}$

$10\frac{1}{6}$
$-4\frac{1}{3}$

$\frac{6}{13}$
$-\frac{1}{3}$

4 The first week of his diet, Hal weighed $150\frac{3}{4}$ pounds. By the second week, his weight had fallen to $149\frac{1}{4}$ pounds. How much weight did Hal lose on his diet? _____

5 The Graham family wants to fly from Detroit, Michigan, to Louisville, Kentucky, next week. They have a choice of 2 flights. One flight takes $3\frac{1}{4}$ hours and the other takes $3\frac{1}{6}$ hours to get to Louisville. How much longer is the first flight than the second? _____

Adding Integers

17

⭐ The sum of two negative numbers is always negative. ⁻3 + (⁻6) = ⁻9

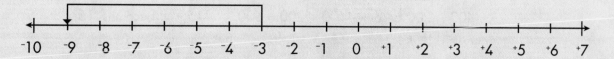

To add numbers with different signs, visualize the numbers on a number line. (⁻800) + 300 = ⁻500

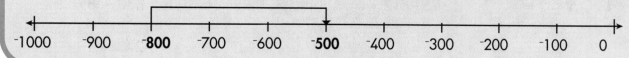

Find the sum.

1   ⁺7 + ⁻3 =   ⁻4 + ⁻8 =   ⁺9 + ⁻2 =   ⁻16 + ⁻8 =

2   6 + ⁻9 =   ⁻11 + ⁺7 =   ⁻3 + ⁻12 =   ⁻8 + ⁺2 =

3   ⁺11 + ⁻6 =   ⁻50.3 + ⁺7.9 =   ⁺789 + ⁻59 =   ⁻6 + ⁻4 =

4   ⁺37 + ⁻47 =   ⁻12 + ⁻16 =   ⁺521 + ⁻387 =   ⁻80 + ⁻30 =

5 The temperature last night was 10° below zero. The next morning by 9:00 A.M., the temperature had risen 12°. What was the temperature at 9:00 A.M.?

_____

6 Bill worked hard and had $500 in his savings account. Last month, he withdrew $80 to buy some CDs, but the following month he deposited $90. Write an addition sentence to find the amount of money he now has.

_____

Subtracting Integers

18

★ To subtract a positive and negative number, switch the sign of the second number and add.

$^+400 - ^-200$ becomes $400 + 200 = 600$. $^-15 - ^-8$ becomes $^-15 + 8 = ^-7$.

Find the difference.

1. $^+5 - ^+2 =$ $^-5 - ^+12 =$ $^-7 - ^+4 =$ $^-30 - ^+8 =$

2. $^-16 - ^+5 =$ $^-2 - ^+9 =$ $^+18 - ^-7 =$ $^-32 - ^-19 =$

3. $^-20 - ^+16 =$ $^+90 - ^+40 =$ $^+7 - ^-86 =$ $^-7 - ^+3 =$

4. $^-5 - ^-2 =$ $^+21 - ^-19 =$ $^+7 - ^-8 =$ $^-76 - ^+14 =$

5. The coldest temperature ever recorded in the United States was $^-79.8°F$ at Prospect Creek in Alaska. The lowest temperature recorded in the lower 48 states was $^-69.7°F$ at Rogers Pass in Montana. What was the difference in temperature between these two locations?

   _____

6. The highest summer temperature average is $92.8°F$ at Death Valley in California. The lowest average winter temperature is $^-15.7°F$ for Barter Island in Alaska. How much warmer is Death Valley than Barter Island?

   _____

7. Death Valley in California is the lowest point in the United States. At its lowest, it is about 300 feet below sea level. If you lived 100 feet above sea level, what would be the change in elevation from your home to the floor of Death Valley?

   _____

Mixed Practice

19

Solve.

Plant	Height (feet)	Flower Width (inches)
Primrose	²⁄₃	½
Black-Eyed Susan	3	2½
Columbine	1⅝	2
Iris	4⅙	2¼
Begonia	1⅞	1⅓
Astilbe	¾	5⅛
Violet	1	⅞

1 What is the difference in height between a columbine and an iris? _____

2 If a begonia grew ½ foot taller, how tall would it be? _____

3 How much wider is the flower of a violet than the flower of a primrose? _____

4 What is the combined height of a black-eyed susan, an astilbe, and a begonia? _____

Country	Area (square kilometers)	Population (2002 estimate)
Argentina	2,766,890	37,812,817
Belize	22,966	262,999
Brazil	8,511,965	176,029,560
Chile	756,950	15,498,930
Colombia	1,138,910	41,008,227
Costa Rica	51,100	3,834,934

5 What is the difference in area between Argentina and Belize? _____

6 What is the combined population of Costa Rica and Brazil? _____

7 What is the difference between the country with the greatest area and the one with the least? _____

8 How many more people live in Colombia than in Chile? _____

Name _____

Mixed Practice

20   Solve.

The world's tallest hospital building is Guys Tower in London. Also known as Guys Hospital, this building has 34 floors above ground and 3 floors below ground.

1   How many floors does this building have? _____

2   If you went from the 25th floor to the second floor below ground, how many floors would you travel? _____

3   If they added 8 floors to the hospital, how far would it be between the top floor and the 13th floor? _____

Add or subtract.

4 $1\frac{5}{6} + 2\frac{5}{8} =$ $5,689,143 + 51,188 =$

5 $\frac{4}{5} + \frac{4}{5} =$ $33,476 - 29,587 =$

6 $^{+}76 + ^{-}35 =$ $43,097 + 856,490 + 44 + 8 =$

Complete the number sentence using < or >.

7 $2\frac{8}{9} + 1\frac{1}{5}$ $\bigcirc$ $2\frac{1}{9} + 1\frac{4}{5}$

8 $^{+}80 + ^{-}25$ $\bigcirc$ $^{-}80 + ^{+}25$

9 $4,893,015 + 68,974$ $\bigcirc$ $4,983,150 - 86,794$

10 $\frac{2}{9} + \frac{3}{10}$ $\bigcirc$ $\frac{2}{10} + \frac{3}{9}$

Name _____

Multiplying Whole Numbers

21 ⭐

```
  7 6 6
  4,867      The first step is to multiply by the 9 in the ones place.
×    39
  43,803     Next, multiply by the 3 in the tens place.
+146,010
  189,813    Last, add.
```

Find the product.

1
432	3,986	81,904	154,654	543
× 33	× 89	× 47	× 64	× 71

2
4,765	983,143	3,800	9,705	198
× 19	× 52	× 23	× 80	× 85

3
115	336	541	83	8,429
× 50	× 12	× 45	×76	× 62

4
332	119	4,187	305	880
× 18	× 99	× 61	× 20	× 50

Use the table to answer the questions.

5 How much would it cost to lease a full-size car for 1 year? _____

6 Antoine's dad wants to get a mid-size car that he plans to keep for 6 years. Which would cost more, buying or leasing the car?_____

Type of Car	Sale Price	Leasing (per month)
Sub-Compact	$11,995	$139
Compact	$16,555	$189
Mid Size	$20,975	$249
Full Size	$25,775	$329
SUV	$28,895	$299

Name _____

Dividing Whole Numbers

22

⭐ First, divide 58 by 23.

```
        256R8
23) 5,896
   − 46
    129
   −115
    146
   −138
      8
```

Next, bring down the 9 and divide 129 by 23.

Last, bring down the 6 and divide 146 by 23.
There is a remainder of 8.

Find the quotient.

1 72)4,735   25)22,125   43)2,749   93)99,956   57)43,781

2 36)1,175   62)18,327   21)15,975   49)15,000   58)76,142

3 14)2,749   17)17,599   41)8,562   30)15,327   32)22,432

4 In 1927, Charles Lindbergh flew from New York to Paris in about 34 hours. If the flight covered 5,780 kilometers, what was Lindbergh's average speed in kilometers per hour? _____

5 In 2003, Tiger Woods won $4,252,420 in 9 golf tournaments. What was his average earnings in each tournament? _____

Multiplying Decimals

23

$$\begin{array}{r} {\scriptstyle 3\;1\;1} \\ 26.22 \\ \times \qquad 5 \\ \hline 131.10 \end{array}$$

To place the decimal point, count the number of decimal places to the right of the decimal in the top number (2). Place the decimal point 2 places from the right in the answer.

$$\begin{array}{r} {\scriptstyle 2\;3} \\ 55.7 \\ \times \quad 4.5 \\ \hline 2785 \\ +22280 \\ \hline 250.65 \end{array}$$

When you multiply two decimals, count the decimal places in each of the numbers. Place the decimal point in the product that many places from the right.

Find the product.

1

$$\begin{array}{r} 679.352 \\ \times \qquad 8 \\ \hline \end{array}$$

$$\begin{array}{r} 229.7 \\ \times \; 25 \\ \hline \end{array}$$

$$\begin{array}{r} 38.73 \\ \times \quad 94 \\ \hline \end{array}$$

$$\begin{array}{r} 78.79 \\ \times \; 6.35 \\ \hline \end{array}$$

$$\begin{array}{r} 41.003 \\ \times \quad 5.9 \\ \hline \end{array}$$

2

$$\begin{array}{r} 7.99 \\ \times 83.28 \\ \hline \end{array}$$

$$\begin{array}{r} 567.8 \\ \times \quad 90 \\ \hline \end{array}$$

$$\begin{array}{r} 13.56 \\ \times 34.6 \\ \hline \end{array}$$

$$\begin{array}{r} 9800 \\ \times \quad 5.3 \\ \hline \end{array}$$

$$\begin{array}{r} 67.42 \\ \times \; 8.8 \\ \hline \end{array}$$

Place the decimal point in the product.

3

$$\begin{array}{r} 34.2 \\ \times \quad 8 \\ \hline 2736 \end{array}$$

$$\begin{array}{r} 567.5 \\ \times \quad 0.5 \\ \hline 28375 \end{array}$$

$$\begin{array}{r} 0.6 \\ \times 5.8 \\ \hline 348 \end{array}$$

$$\begin{array}{r} 98.12 \\ \times \; 6.20 \\ \hline 608344 \end{array}$$

$$\begin{array}{r} 81.3 \\ \times \; 0.34 \\ \hline 27642 \end{array}$$

4

$$\begin{array}{r} 0.5 \\ \times 55 \\ \hline 275 \end{array}$$

$$\begin{array}{r} 4.713 \\ \times \qquad 8 \\ \hline 37704 \end{array}$$

$$\begin{array}{r} 1452 \\ \times \; 0.96 \\ \hline 139392 \end{array}$$

$$\begin{array}{r} 280 \\ \times 0.6 \\ \hline 168 \end{array}$$

$$\begin{array}{r} 17 \\ \times \; 0.23 \\ \hline 391 \end{array}$$

---

5 A human heart beats an average of 65 times per minute. How many times would a human heart beat in 6.8 minutes? _____

6 A Major League pitcher allowed an average of 4.15 runs per game. If he pitched in 28 games, how many runs would he allow? _____

Dividing Decimals

24

$$\begin{array}{r} 3.8 \\ 4\overline{)15.2} \\ -12 \\ \hline 32 \\ -32 \\ \hline 0 \end{array}$$

Place the decimal point in the quotient above the decimal point in the number you are dividing.

$$\begin{array}{r} 1\,9. \\ 4.5\overline{)85.5} \\ -45 \\ \hline 405 \\ -405 \\ \hline 0 \end{array}$$

If both your **divisor** (the number you are dividing by) and **dividend** (the number you are dividing) contain decimals, count the number of decimal places in the divisor. Move the decimal point that many places to the right in the dividend. Then, bring the decimal point straight up.

Find the quotient.

1 $2\overline{)40.62}$ $4\overline{)941.2}$ $23\overline{)128.8}$ $2.4\overline{)5.28}$ $5.1\overline{)20.4}$

2 $5.3\overline{)88.51}$ $15\overline{)954.45}$ $4.6\overline{)8,765.3}$ $31\overline{)3,095.72}$ $2.3\overline{)73.6}$

3 $98\overline{)121.03}$ $20.7\overline{)107.64}$ $7.7\overline{)480.48}$ $34\overline{)37.91}$ $15\overline{)489.36}$

4 A garden is 80.60 feet wide. If a fence post will be placed every 6.2 feet, how many posts will be needed along the back side of the garden? _____

5 Jill has a large jar that holds 64.8 ounces of flour. If she wants to pour the flour into 8-ounce cups, how many cups will she need? _____

Multiplying Fractions and Mixed Numbers

25

⭐ What is the product of $\frac{3}{4} \times 28$?

First, write 28 as a fraction and then multiply the numerators and denominators:

$$\frac{28}{1} \times \frac{3}{4} = \frac{84}{4} = 21$$

What is the product of $\frac{3}{5} \times 2\frac{1}{2}$?

First, convert $2\frac{1}{2}$ to an improper fraction and then multiply:

$$\frac{5}{2} \times \frac{3}{5} = \frac{15}{10} = 1\frac{5}{10} = 1\frac{1}{2}$$

Express the product in simplest terms.

1 $\frac{4}{5} \times \frac{5}{6} =$ $\qquad$ $18 \times \frac{2}{3} =$ $\qquad$ $\frac{1}{4} \times \frac{2}{7} =$

2 $2\frac{2}{3} \times \frac{5}{9} =$ $\qquad$ $5\frac{1}{8} \times 3\frac{2}{3} =$ $\qquad$ $\frac{6}{7} \times \frac{8}{9} =$

3 $2\frac{4}{5} \times 1\frac{2}{3} =$ $\qquad$ $6\frac{1}{9} \times 15 =$ $\qquad$ $\frac{7}{8} \times \frac{2}{5} =$

4 $9\frac{3}{8} \times 4\frac{4}{5} =$ $\qquad$ $5\frac{1}{2} \times \frac{1}{6} =$ $\qquad$ $\frac{5}{6} \times 1\frac{1}{3} =$

5 A recipe for lasagna that serves 4 people calls for ⅓ cup of olive oil. If you wanted to make lasagna for 12 people, how much olive oil would you need? _____

6 Brenda completed ½ of her 10-mile hike by noon. By noon, Ted had completed ⅔ of his 9-mile hike. Who had walked a greater distance? _____

Dividing Fractions and Mixed Numbers

26

⭐ To divide a fraction, reverse the numerator and denominator of the second fraction, then multiply.

$$\frac{4}{1} \div \frac{1}{2} = \frac{4}{1} \times \frac{2}{1} = \frac{8}{1} = 8$$

Express the quotient in simplest terms.

1 $\frac{2}{5} \div \frac{1}{10} =$ $12 \div \frac{3}{5} =$ $\frac{7}{12} \div \frac{2}{3} =$

2 $\frac{2}{3} \div 1\frac{1}{8} =$ $7 \div \frac{1}{3} =$ $\frac{9}{10} \div \frac{1}{2} =$

3 $3\frac{2}{3} \div \frac{5}{6} =$ $4\frac{2}{7} \div 2\frac{1}{3} =$ $3\frac{4}{7} \div 9 =$

4 $7 \div \frac{5}{8} =$ $1\frac{3}{4} \div \frac{1}{2} =$ $\frac{5}{12} \div \frac{2}{3} =$

5   Carla worked out at the gym for $4\frac{1}{2}$ hours yesterday. If she took a break every $\frac{1}{2}$ hour, how many breaks did Carla take?

_____

6   A garden snail crawls at $^3/_{100}$ mile per hour. How long would it take the snail to crawl $\frac{1}{2}$ mile? Express your answer in simplest terms.

_____

7   A $10\frac{1}{2}$-ounce box of cereal costs $2.31. How much does the cereal cost per ounce?

_____

Multiplying Integers

27

⭐ A positive number multiplied by a negative number will always result in a negative number. $30 \times {}^-6 = {}^-180$

A negative number multiplied by a negative number is always positive. ${}^-8 \times {}^-3 = 24$

A positive number multiplied by a positive number is always positive. $12 \times 8 = 96$

Find the product.

1

${}^-15$	127	${}^-8$	${}^-18$	${}^-547$
$\times\ \ 8$	$\times\ 63$	$\times\ {}^-4$	$\times\ {}^-15$	$\times\ \ 17$

2

$6,548$	57	789	${}^-85$	${}^-127$
$\times\ \ \ 34$	$\times\ {}^-22$	$\times\ \ 23$	$\times\ {}^-16$	$\times\ \ 13$

3

400	${}^-28$	85	90	${}^-76$
$\times\ {}^-50$	$\times\ \ 7$	$\times 45$	$\times\ {}^-9$	$\times\ {}^-25$

Some of the following problems have a product with an incorrect sign. If the product is correct, circle it. If not, write the correct sign.

4 ${}^-8 \times 7 = 56$ ${}^-12 \times {}^-7 = 84$ ${}^-5 \times 3 = {}^-15$ $20 \times 5 = 100$

5 ${}^-9 \times 4 = 36$ ${}^-2 \times {}^-20 = 40$ ${}^-15 \times 5 = {}^-75$ ${}^-6 \times {}^-9 = 54$

6   Some people have money automatically taken out of their bank accounts to pay their bills. This saves them the trouble of writing checks. Suppose your monthly car payment is $200, which is taken out each month. If payments are made for 5 months, how much will be taken out of your bank account?

_____

Name _____

Dividing Integers

28

⭐ A negative number divided by a positive number results in a negative number. $^-72 \div 8 = ^-9$

A positive number divided by a positive number is always positive. $30 \div 5 = 6$

A negative number divided by another negative number is always positive. $^-16 \div ^-2 = 8$

Find the quotient.

1. $^-70 \div ^-10 =$ $^-35 \div 5 =$ $28 \div ^-4 =$ $64 \div ^-2 =$

2. $^-10 \div ^-2 =$ $90 \div ^-3 =$ $121 \div ^-11 =$ $90 \div 9 =$

3. $^-49 \div 7 =$ $70 \div ^-5 =$ $125 \div 5 =$ $200 \div ^-20 =$

4. $^-80 \div 8 =$ $^-64 \div ^-2 =$ $^-80 \div 5 =$ $70 \div ^-2 =$

Some of the following problems have a quotient with an incorrect sign. If the quotient is correct, circle it. If not, write the correct sign.

5. $^-100 \div ^-10 = 10$ $20 \div ^-5 = 4$ $^-60 \div 6 = ^-10$ $56 \div 2 = ^-28$

6. $^-42 \div ^-6 = ^-7$ $30 \div 5 = 6$ $^-80 \div 5 = 16$ $^-42 \div 6 = 7$

7. Carl loves to go scuba diving in Florida. He wanted to explore the Barracuda Reef, which lies 35 feet below the ocean's surface. If Carl rests every 7 feet as he descends, how many times will he rest? Solve this problem using positive and negative numbers. _____

8. Harriet lost 20 pounds in the last 5 months on her diet. How much weight has she lost each month? Solve this problem using positive and negative numbers.

_____

Name _____

29

Solve.

1 562.3 x 7 =   3,236 x 47 =   29,006 ÷ 53 =   290.06 ÷ 35 =

2 $\frac{4}{5} \div 15 =$ $7\frac{5}{8} \times \frac{3}{4} =$ $\frac{1}{3} \times \frac{3}{8} =$

3 $\begin{array}{r} 115 \\ \times\ 50 \\ \hline \end{array}$ $\begin{array}{r} 541 \\ \times\ 45 \\ \hline \end{array}$ $\begin{array}{r} 8,429 \\ \times\quad 62 \\ \hline \end{array}$

4 23 x ⁻8 =   ⁻51 x ⁻6 =   83 x ⁻62 =   ⁻46 ÷ ⁻2 =   ⁻36 ÷ 4 =

5 Jamie went surfing in the ocean right after a storm. Each time she got hit by a wave, Jamie was pushed back 15 feet. If Jamie got hit by 3 waves in a row, how far back was she pushed? _____

6 The Appalachian Trail is a hiking trail stretching for over 2,000 miles from Georgia to Maine. The largest portion of the trail, 363.9 miles, is in Virginia. How much of the trail is outside Virginia? _____

7 If a hiker leaves the trail to rest after one-third of the Virgina part is completed, how many miles will he or she have hiked? _____

8 One hiker averaged 22.8 miles per day. If he continued this pace for 35 days, how far did he hike? _____

Name _____

30

Solve.

1 $60,450 \div 62 =$ $^-3.78 \times 0.25 =$ $^-912 \div ^-76 =$ $57,262 \times 35 =$

2 $\dfrac{3}{8} \times \dfrac{2}{3} =$ $12 \div 1\dfrac{1}{2} =$ $\dfrac{4}{5} \div \dfrac{1}{6} =$

3 $3\dfrac{4}{5} \div 2\dfrac{1}{4} =$ $9 \times \dfrac{3}{5} =$ $4\dfrac{1}{7} \times 2\dfrac{2}{3} =$

4 $144 \div ^-12 =$ $^-518 \div ^-37 =$ $241 \times ^-36 =$ $545 \times 15 =$

5 Last week, Noel painted his room on Monday, Wednesday, and Saturday. If he painted for 2¾ hours each day, how much time did Noel spend painting last week?

_____

6 Jack can run 2 miles in 12½ minutes. How long will it take him to run 6 miles?

_____

7 As you climb higher up a mountain, the temperature drops. In fact, for every 1,000 feet gained in elevation, the temperature falls by 3½°F. If you gained 6,000 feet in elevation, how much would the temperature decrease? _____

8 Andy is serving ice cream to his friends. If he has 6½ pints of ice cream and he wants to give each person 1½ cups of ice cream, how many friends can Andy serve? (Hint: 2 cups = 1 pint) _____

Name _____

Solving Problems

31

Use the tables to answer the questions.

1 How far will sound travel in 18 seconds if the air temperature is 15°C?

Air Temperature	Speed of Sound
Air at 0°C	331 meters per second
Air at 15°C	340 meters per second
Air at 30°C	349 meters per second

_____

2 If sound travels 3,972 meters in 12 seconds, what is the air temperature?

_____

3 The air temperature is 30°C. Jake yells toward a wall and it takes 2 seconds for the echo to reach him. How far away is the wall from Jake?

_____

4 How much farther will sound travel in air for 20 seconds at 15°C as compared to air at 0°C?

_____

Country	Population Density (measure of the number of people living in a square mile)
Australia	5.39
Denmark	300.67
Ghana	152.01
Laos	43.749
Panama	67.202
Zambia	24.08

5 If the area of Panama is 29,761 square miles, how many people live in Panama?

_____

6 If a census is taken of an area covering 89.4 square miles in Laos, about how many people would be counted?

_____

7 There are about 9.48 times as many people living per square mile in Venezuela as compared to Australia. What is the population density of Venezuela?

_____

Advantage Math Grade 6 © 2004 Creative Teaching Press

Name _____

Solving Problems

32

Solve the problems. Use the table to answer questions 5 and 6.

1 Earth is about 150 million kilometers from the sun. The next closest planet to the sun, Venus, is about $\frac{7}{10}$ as far from the sun as Earth. About how far is Venus from the sun?

_____

2 After Earth, the next farthest planet from the sun is Mars. This planet is about $1\frac{1}{2}$ times as far from the sun as compared to Earth. About how far from the sun is Mars?

_____

3 Mammals come in many sizes. The mouse lemur grows to an adult length of about 10 inches, while the blue whale can grow to a length of 91 feet and weigh 90 tons. If a young mouse lemur is $\frac{1}{8}$ the length of a full-grown adult, how long is it?

_____

4 A blue whale needs to grow $1\frac{1}{2}$ times its current weight to reach its full weight of 90 tons. How much does the blue whale weigh?

_____

Cave	Depth (meters)
Voronja	1,710
Torca del Cerro	1,589
Sistema Huautla	1,475
Boy-Bulok	1,415
Ceki	1,380

5 If a cave is one-fourth the depth of Ceki, how deep is the cave?

_____

6 Voronja is about $1\frac{1}{4}$ times as deep as Sistema Huautla. About how far below the surface is this cave?

_____

Solving Problems

33

Use the scorecard to answer questions 1–4. Use the recipe to answer 5–7.

Scorecard

Hole	1	2	3	4	5	6	7	8	9	Total
Yards	421	173	509	544	139	297	355	433	391	
Par	4	3	5	5	3	4	4	4	4	

1 The scorecard shows the length of each hole. What is the total yardage for 9 holes? ____

2 How much greater is the yardage of the 9th hole than the 6th hole? _____

3 In golf, par is the number of strokes you are supposed to take on a hole. Using the scorecard above, for example, on the 3rd hole, you should take 5 strokes. If you take 4 strokes, you will score a birdie, or 1 under par. This can also be expressed as a score of ⁻1. If Jeff scored ⁻2 for the 9 holes, what was his total score? _____

4 Jeff's playing partner, Fred, scored 4 over par. How much higher was his score than Jeff's score? _____

Rice Pudding Recipe

RICE PUDDING
1½ cup cooked rice
1¼ cup skim milk
2/3 cup raisins
½ teaspoon vanilla extract
⅛ teaspoon nutmeg
4 Teaspoons sugar
1/3 teaspoon cinnamon

5 For easy handling, Paula plans to put the rice into 2 bowls. How much rice will be in each bowl?

_____

6 Paula poured the skim milk into a glass. If she poured out ½ cup, how much milk was left in the glass?

_____

7 This recipe makes 2 servings, but if Paula wants to serve 6 people, how many cups of raisins will she need?

_____

Solving Problems

34 Solve.

First 6 Stages of the Race

Stage	Distance (kilometers)
1	168
2	204.5
3	167.5
4	69
5	196.5
6	230

1 What is the total distance covered in the first 6 stages of the race? _____

2 If a racer completed the 4th stage in 1½ hours, what is his average speed? _____

3 A kilometer is equal to 0.621 mile. How many miles is Stage 3? _____

4 The 13th stage is about 1.17 times as long as the 1st stage. How many kilometers is the 13th stage of the race? _____

There are five species of rhinoceros in the world living in Africa and Asia. The largest is the white rhinoceros with a height of 6 feet 5 inches (198 centimeters). The smallest is the Sumatran rhinoceros with a height of 4 feet 4 inches (132 centimeters).

5 About what percent of the height of the white rhinoceros is the Sumatran rhinoceros?

_____

6 The black rhinoceros is about 75% of the size of the white rhinoceros. How tall is the black rhinoceros? _____

7 An adult black rhinoceros can weigh more than 1,000 pounds. If a baby is born at 1% of this weight, how much does a baby black rhinoceros weigh? _____

Order of Operations

35

⭐ In the order of operations, multiplication and division are performed before addition or subtraction.

$$12 \times 3 + 5$$

First, multiply. $12 \times 3 = 36$

Add 5. $36 + 5 = 41$

Operations inside parentheses are performed before multiplication or division. $15 + (8 \times 4) + 10$

$$15 + 32 + 10 = 57$$

Evaluate the following expressions.

1 $8 \times 7 + 5 =$

2 $63 \div 9 - 2 =$

3 $6 + 3 \times 8 =$

4 $20 - 8 \div 2 =$

5 $20 \div (2 + 3) + 5 =$

6 $50 \div (4 + 1) \times 6 =$

7 $(7 + 2) \times (9 - 5) =$

8 $6 + 15 \div 3 + (8 - 2) =$

9 $(8 - 6) \times 7 + (5 \times 5) =$

10 $(6 + 8) \div 2 + 4 \times 8 =$

Name _____

Order of Operations

36

 To remember the order of operations, think of the acronym PEMDAS:

Parentheses
Exponents
Multiplication or **D**ivision from left to right
Addition or **S**ubtraction from left to right

$20 \div 2 + (5 - 2) \times 4^2 = ?$

P $20 \div 2 + 3 \times 4^2$
E $20 \div 2 + 3 \times 16$
M $20 \div 2 + 48$
D $10 + 48$
A 58

Evaluate the following expressions.

1 $12 \times 3 - (8 + 4) \div 2^2 =$

2 $9 + 6 \times (7 - 3) \times 2^3 =$

3 $3^3 \times (6 + 4) - 5 + 10 =$

Which expression has the greater value? Use > or <.

4 $(8 + 7) \times 6 + 3^2 \bigcirc 8 + (7 \times 6) + 3^2$

5 $3 \times 5 + (2^2 - 1) + 9 \bigcirc 3 \times (5 + 2^2) - 1 + 9$

6 $4^2 \times 2 \times 5 + (3 + 4) - 2 \bigcirc 4^2 \times 2 \times (5 + 3) + 4 - 2$

7 $15 + (9 \times 3) - 3^3 \bigcirc (15 + 9) \times 3 - 3^2$

Add the operation signs and parentheses where needed.

8 $6 \quad 5 \quad 9 \quad 2 \quad = 77$

9 $7^2 \quad 8 \quad 6 \quad 3 \quad = 59$

10 $8 \quad 6 \quad 4 \quad = 44$

Follow the order of operations and find the missing number.

11 $20 + 5 \times (? + 6) - 12 \div 2 = 64$

Mixed Practice

37

Complete the tables.

There is a way of measuring your health risks related to weight. It is known as your Body Mass Index (BMI). Finding your BMI is done by following this formula:

BMI = Weight x 703 ÷ height (inches) ÷ height (inches)

If your BMI is greater than 27 or less than 19, you may have an increased risk of health problems.

1 Find the BMI for these people and complete the chart. Do they have a health risk?

Name	Height (Inches)	Weight	BMI	Health Risk
Arnie	72	180		
Jackie	63	162		
Rochelle	67	190		
Tim	75	206		
Michelle	58	135		

2 The table below lists the population of several states based on the 2000 census. Evaluate the expressions to find the population of each state. When you are done, rank the states from 1 to 6, from least to greatest.

State	Population	Population	Rank
Arizona	$(64,125 \times 10) \times 2^3$		
Colorado	$134,375 \times 4 \times (6 + 2)$		
Illinois	$(15 - 7) \times 2^2 \times 387,500$		
Missouri	$11,200 \times (5 - 1) \times 125$		
Oregon	$5^2 \times (20 \div 2) \times 13,600$		
Washington	$(41 + 18) \times (13 - 3) \times 10^4$		

Mixed Practice

38

Solve.

1. The cheetah can run up to 70 mph. Mike showed the speed of the cheetah using the following expression: $3^4 + 11$. What was Mike's mistake?

_____

2. The number of cheetahs living in Namibia, Africa, may be expressed as $(3^2 - 7) \times 10^3$. How many cheetahs live in Namibia?

_____

3. In all, today there are about 25,000 cheetahs living in Africa. In the past, there were at least $30 \times 2^2 \times (20 + 5) \times (28 - 3)$ cheetahs. How many more cheetahs were there in the past? _____

Each of the symbols in this chart has a numeric value. Use the order of operations to find the value of each symbol.

✸ +	✦ x	▭	75
x ✦ x	x ▭ −	÷ ✸	69
+ ▭ ÷	+ ✸ +	+ ✦	11
33	75	11	

✸ =   ✦ =   ▭ =

Name _____

Take a Test Drive

Fill in the bubble beside the correct answer.

---

1 Which expression has a product of ⁻7.56?

- ○ ⁻2.7 x ⁻2.8
- ○ 2.7 x ⁻2.8
- ○ 2.7 x 2.8
- ○ 2.7 x ⁻0.28

5 What is the product of 47,856 x 29?

- ○ 1,187,315
- ○ 1,218,319
- ○ 1,416,842
- ○ 1,387,824

---

2 What is the product of ⁻56 x ⁻83?

- ○ ⁻4,648
- ○ 4,846
- ○ 4,648
- ○ ⁻4,846

6 What is the quotient of 82,838 ÷ 97?

- ○ 854
- ○ 876
- ○ 836
- ○ 848

---

3 Find the value of (5 + 9) ÷ 2 + 3.

- ○ 10
- ○ 60
- ○ 15
- ○ 45

7 What is the product of 453.28 x 7.5?

- ○ 33,996
- ○ 33.996
- ○ 339.96
- ○ 3,399.6

---

4 What is the missing number?
6 + (? x 3) ÷ 3 + 8 x (2 x 6) = 105

- ○ 3
- ○ 2
- ○ 5
- ○ 4

8 What is the quotient of 92.4 ÷ 0.2?

- ○ 46.2
- ○ 462
- ○ 4.62
- ○ 4,620

Name _____

Take a Test Drive

Fill in the bubble beside the correct answer.

---

1 There are (500 + 300) x (5 + 3) windows in the Empire State Building. How many windows does the Empire State Building have?

- ○ 1,600
- ○ 3,400
- ○ 6,400
- ○ 8,100

2 Elevators in the building needed to travel at a speed of 1,200 feet per minute to deliver 15,000 people a day. This was $1\frac{3}{4}$ times faster than any elevator had ever traveled. What was the speed of the older elevator?

- ○ about 695 feet per second
- ○ about 635 feet per second
- ○ about 686 feet per second
- ○ about 612 feet per second

3 The building cost was about $40,000,000, which was less than the original expectation. If the completed cost was $\frac{4}{5}$ of the expected cost, what was the expected cost of the project?

- ○ $45,000,000
- ○ $50,000,000
- ○ $55,000,000
- ○ $32,000,000

4 $6\frac{1}{8} + 3\frac{1}{4} =$

- ○ $9\frac{3}{8}$
- ○ 9
- ○ $8\frac{1}{4}$
- ○ $9\frac{5}{8}$

5 The summit of Mauna Loa rises to a height of 13,677 feet. To convert this to meters, divide by 3.28. About how many meters high is Mauna Loa?

- ○ about 4,170 meters
- ○ about 41,170 meters
- ○ about 417 meters
- ○ about 417,000 meters

6 The summit of Kilauea is about $\frac{3}{10}$ the elevation of Mauna Loa. What is the elevation of Kilauea?

- ○ about 3,800 feet
- ○ about 4,100 feet
- ○ about 4,000 feet
- ○ about 4,200 feet

7 The visitor center is open $64\frac{3}{4}$ hours a week, 52 weeks a year. How many hours is the visitors center open during the year?

- ○ 3,117 hours
- ○ 3,434 hours
- ○ 3,237 hours
- ○ 3,367 hours

Using Estimation

41

⭐ One car averaged 48.75 miles per hour while another car averaged 53.90 miles per hour. What is the difference in their speeds?

$$\begin{array}{r} 53.90 \\ -48.75 \\ \hline 5.15 \end{array} \text{ miles per hour}$$

You can use estimation to check if your answer makes sense. Round each of the numbers to the nearest whole number and subtract.

53.90 rounds to 54
48.75 rounds to 49
54 − 49 = 5

You know your answer should be near 5, so your answer of 5.15 is reasonable.

Write a sentence or two to answer each item.

1 Paula bikes a total of 6 miles to and from school. At the end of the 183-day school year, Paula found that she had biked 1,098 miles. Using estimation, explain if her answer is reasonable.

_____

_____

2 An astronaut needs to consume 3,021 calories a day to survive in space. If a space mission lasts 21 days, the astronaut will need to consume 6,340 calories. Does this answer make sense? Use estimation to explain your answer.

_____

_____

3 The busiest airport in the world is O'Hare Airport in Chicago, Illinois. About 2,000 planes and jets land and take off there each day. Would 37,111 takeoffs and landings in 17 days be a reasonable answer? Use estimation to explain your answer.

_____

_____

4 Danielle worked for 31 hours. She earned $12 per hour. After she got paid, she bought a CD for $16.99 and a video for $12.50. Is it reasonable to say Danielle had about $340 left when she was done shopping? Use estimation to help explain your answer.

_____

_____

Exact Answers and Estimates

42

⭐ At times, you need to find an exact answer, but other times an estimate is fine. If you only need an estimate to solve the problem, then estimate the answer and tell why. If you need an exact answer to solve the problem, then calculate it and tell why.

Circle one choice.

1 A tailor is making 3 coats, which take 5¾ yards of material each. If the tailor has 20 yards of material, is there enough to make the coats?

EXACT   ESTIMATE

_____

_____

2 Four players on the Baltimore Orioles have 13, 21, 19, and 14 home runs. Four players on the Seattle Mariners have 19, 15, 25, and 26 home runs. Is the Mariners' home run total greater than the home run total of the 4 players on the Orioles?

EXACT   ESTIMATE

_____

_____

3 The average precipitation in New York City for a year is 49.69 inches. This year, precipitation has totaled 56.32. How much above normal is the precipitation this year?

EXACT   ESTIMATE

_____

_____

4 Alexandra buys 4 packages of paper for $1.29 each and a notebook for $2.75. If she pays with a $10 bill, how much change will she receive?

EXACT   ESTIMATE

_____

_____

Prime and Composite Numbers

43

⭐ A **prime number** has 2 factors, itself and 1. These are some examples of prime numbers:

$7 = 7 \times 1$ $19 = 19 \times 1$ $79 = 79 \times 1$

A **composite number** is a number that has more than 2 factors. These are some examples of composite numbers:

$15 = 15 \times 1$ $15 = 5 \times 3$
$32 = 32 \times 1$ $32 = 16 \times 2$ $32 = 8 \times 4$

Every even number greater than 2 is a composite number.
The number 1 is neither prime nor composite.

Tell whether each number is prime or composite, then show the factors for each number.

1 21 _____   _____

2 41 _____   _____

3 50 _____   _____

4 25 _____   _____

5 48 _____   _____

6 Circle the numbers that are prime.   23 24 27 29

7 Circle the numbers that are NOT prime.   53 56 61 81

8 Why is 2 the only even prime number?

_____

_____

Greatest Common Factor

44

 Factors are numbers that when multiplied by another number, result in a product.

For example, 6 and 4 are factors of 24, since 6 x 4 = 24. 12 and 2 are also factors of 24, since 12 x 2 = 24. 24, 1, 8, and 3 are also factors of 24. You can say the factors of 24 are 24, 12, 8, 6, 4, 3, 2, and 1.

The **greatest common factor** (**GCF**) is the largest factor that is shared by two numbers.

48 – 1, 2, 3, 4, 6, **8**, 12, 24, 48   64 – 1, 2, 4, **8**, 16, 32, 64

You see that 8 is the largest factor that both 48 and 64 have in common.
8 x 6 = 48   8 x 8 = 64

Show the factors of each number.

1 40 _____

2 18 _____

3 28 _____

4 56 _____

Find the greatest common factor. Show the factors of each number.

5 24 and 30 _____

6 36 and 54 _____

7 16 and 56 _____

8 40 and 60 _____

Name _____

Least Common Multiple

45

⭐ A **multiple** is the product of two numbers.

3   3, 6, 9, 12, **15**
5   5, 10, **15**

The smallest common multiple of two or more numbers is known as the **least common multiple (LCM)**.

Find the least common multiple of these numbers.

1 8, 12 _____   7, 14 _____

2 15, 40 _____   14, 44 _____

3 3, 5, 12 _____   4, 8, 16 _____

4 3, 6, 9 _____   2, 6, 24 _____

5 2, 8, 10 _____   12, 36, 72 _____

6 The least common multiple for a number and 6 is 24. What is the number? _____

7 Each package of hamburgers has 8 hamburgers and each package of buns has 6 buns. What is the least number of packages of hamburgers and buns you would buy to have an equal number of hamburgers and buns? _____

8 The Greek mathematician Eratosthenes invented a method of finding all the prime numbers between 1 and 100. Follow the instructions shown below.

- List the numbers from 1 to 100 on a separate piece of paper.
- Cross out 1.
- Cross out all the multiples of 2 that are greater than 2.
- Cross out all the multiples of 3 that are greater than 3.
- Cross out all the multiples of 5 that are greater than 5.
- Cross out all the multiples of 7 that are greater than 7.

The remaining numbers are all prime.

Name _____

Prime Factorization

46

⭐ Any composite number is the product of prime numbers. This is known as **the prime factorization** of the number. Two of the factors of 50 are 10 and 5, since 10 x 5 = 50. 5 is a prime number, but 10 is a composite number that is the product of 5 x 2. You can say the prime factorization of 50 is 5 x 5 x 2.

What is the prime factorization of 60?

Prime factorization can also be shown using a **factor tree**.

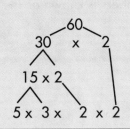

The prime factorization of 60 is 5 x 3 x 2 x 2. This can also be written as $5 \times 3 \times 2^2$.

Show the prime factorization of these numbers.

1 24   36

2 20   49

---

3 Many people don't realize that the Statue of Liberty was not built in the United States. The statue, a gift from France to the people of the United States, was built in separate pieces in France and shipped across the Atlantic Ocean in 214 crates. It was then assembled on an island in New York Harbor. Using a factor tree, find the prime factorization of 214.

4 The prime factors of a number are greater than 5 and less than 13. What is the number? _____

5 If a number is a prime factor of 27, will it also be a prime factor of 54? Explain your answer. _____

Divisibility Rules

47 If you know the rules of divisibility, you will know instantly whether a number is divisible by another number. One number is **divisible** by another number if there is no remainder when you divide.

Number	Rule	Example
2	The number ends in an even number (0, 2, 4, 6, 8)	4**28**
3	The sum of the digits is divisible by 3	243 **2 + 4 + 3 = 9**
4	The number formed by the last 2 digits is divisible by 4	5**36**
5	The number ends in 0 or 5	35**0** or 47**5**
6	The number is divisible by 2 or 3	528 — the last digit is an even number and the sum of the digits is 15, which is divisible by 3
9	The sum of the digits is divisible by 9	648 **6 + 4 + 8 = 18**
10	The number ends in 0	91**0**

Tell if each number is divisible by 2, 3, 4, 5, 6, 9, or 10. Some numbers may be divisible by more than one number. Explain your answer.

1 372 _____

2 891 _____

3 580 _____

4 928 _____

5 Aztec Peak in Arizona is the highest mountain in the Sierra Ancha Mountain Range. If the elevation of Aztec Peak is divisible by 2, is the elevation 7,963 or 7,964 feet? Explain your answer, using the rules of divisibility. _____

6 Mount Baldy is the highest peak in the White Mountains of eastern Arizona. Its elevation is divisible by 3 and 9. Is the elevation 11,603; 11,503; or 11,403 feet? Explain your answer, using the rules of divisibility. _____

Name _____

Divisibility Rules

48

Fill in the table. Write **yes** or **no**.

1

Number	4,650	3,820	1,638	5,124	8,145
Divisible by 2					
Divisible by 3					
Divisible by 4					
Divisible by 5					
Divisible by 6					
Divisible by 9					
Divisible by 10					

Write **true** or **false**.

2   If a number is divisible by 2, it is divisible by 4. _____

3   All numbers that are divisible by 5 are also divisible by 10. _____

4   All numbers that are divisible by 9 are odd numbers. _____

5   Some numbers that are divisible by 3 are even numbers. _____

Find the mystery number.

6   What is a number that is between 40 and 60 that is divisible by 2, 3, 4, and 6?
_____

7   It is less than 100,000. It's an even number. It is divisible by 2, 3, and 6. None of the digits is less than 4. None of the digits is used more than once. The sum of the digits is 30. The digit in the hundreds place is two less than the digit in the thousands place. The digit in the ten-thousands place is one more than the digit in the thousands place. The digit in the tens place is one less than the digit in the hundreds place. If the number were increased by 6, it would be divisible by 2, 3, 4, 6, and 9. _____

Take a Test Drive

Fill in the bubble beside the correct answer.

1 What are all the composite factors of 40?
- ○ 2, 5
- ○ 4, 8, 10, 20, 40
- ○ 4, 8, 10, 15, 20
- ○ 2, 5, 8, 10, 20, 40

2 What are all the prime factors of 60?
- ○ 2, 5, 3
- ○ 6, 10
- ○ 2, 3, 4
- ○ 5, 15, 20

3 Numbers may be written as the sum of two prime numbers. What are two prime numbers that when added together make 40?
- ○ 15 and 25
- ○ 16 and 24
- ○ 19 and 21
- ○ 17 and 23

4 What numbers are between 20 and 30 with a GCF of 3?
- ○ 21, 24, 27
- ○ 21, 24, 28
- ○ 21, 25, 27
- ○ 21, 2, 29

5 What two numbers are between 1 and 20 with a LCM of 36?
- ○ 9 and 18
- ○ 4 and 9
- ○ 4 and 6
- ○ 4 and 8

6 What numbers are between 10 and 40 with a GCF of 6 and a LCM of 90?
- ○ 15 and 30
- ○ 12 and 24
- ○ 18 and 30
- ○ 30 and 45

7 A total of 3,145 pounds of newspapers has been collected in a recycling drive. If you want to divide these newspapers into even piles, how many piles should you have?
- ○ 3
- ○ 4
- ○ 5
- ○ 6

8 Which number is divisible by 9?
- ○ 772
- ○ 989
- ○ 593
- ○ 603

Take a Test Drive

Fill in the bubble beside the correct answer.

1 There will be 336 people at a fund raising dinner. If organizers want an equal number of people at each table, how many people could be seated at each table?

- ○ 2, 4, 6, 8
- ○ 1, 3, 5, 7, 9
- ○ 10, 12, 14, 16
- ○ 11, 13, 15, 17

2 For the last 12 years, the average enrollment for a college has been 5,165 students. Which would be a reasonable estimate of the total enrollment for 12 years?

- ○ 500,000
- ○ 50,000
- ○ 100,000
- ○ 600,000

3 Mirror primes are pairs of prime numbers whose digits are reversed. For example, 37 and 73 are mirror primes. Which of the following number pairs is a mirror prime?

- ○ 15 and 51
- ○ 79 and 97
- ○ 18 and 81
- ○ 39 and 93

4 Twin primes are prime numbers with a difference of 2. For example, (5, 3) is a twin prime. Which of the following numbers is a twin prime?

- ○ (4, 7)
- ○ (7, 9)
- ○ (5, 7)
- ○ (7, 11)

5 Each month, 26,018 copies of a magazine are sold. About how many copies are sold in a year?

- ○ 300,000
- ○ 30,000
- ○ 3,000,000
- ○ 30,000,000

6 The prime factors of a number are between 13 and 23. What is the number?

- ○ 221
- ○ 323
- ○ 299
- ○ 437

7 The least common multiple of three different numbers is 40. What are the numbers?

- ○ 5, 8, and 30
- ○ 5, 8, and 10
- ○ 4, 6, and 10
- ○ 2, 4, and 8

8 The prime factors of two numbers are 2, 3, and 7. Some of the factors may be used more than once. If the numbers are between 1 and 100, what are the two numbers?

- ○ 21 and 63
- ○ 16 and 35
- ○ 45 and 56
- ○ 42 and 84

Determining Perimeter

51

⭐ **Perimeter** is the distance around a figure. To find the perimeter of any square, use the formula $P = 4s$, where s is the length of the side.

For any figure with sides of equal length, you can use the formula $P = \text{number of sides} \times \text{the length of each side}$.

For finding the perimeter of a rectangle, you can use the formula $P = (2 \times \text{width}) + (2 \times \text{length})$.

1 What is the perimeter of the triangle? _____   8 ft   8 ft
   8 ft

2 What is the perimeter of the square? _____   6 cm
   6 cm

3 What is the perimeter of the rectangle? _____   3 m
   4 m

4 What is the perimeter of the rectangle? _____   10 ft
   16 ft

5 The perimeter of a rectangle is 50 feet. What could be the length and width of this rectangle?

_____

6 A rectangle is 5 feet long and has a perimeter of 14 feet. What is the width of this rectangle?

_____

7 A pentagon is a five-sided figure. If a pentagon has a perimeter of 40 yards and the sides are of equal length, what is the length of each of its sides?

_____

Name _____

Determining Area

52

⭐ The **area** is the number of square units needed to cover a figure.

Area of a Square

A = side x side
A = s x s
A = 5 x 5 = 25
The area is 25 sq cm or 25 cm².

5 cm

Area of a Rectangle

A = length x width
A = l x w
A = 8 x 5 = 40
The area is 40 sq cm or 40 cm².

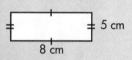
5 cm
8 cm

Find the area.

1

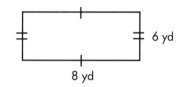
6 yd
8 yd

$A = l \times w$
$A =$ _____ x _____
$A =$ _____

12 in.

$A = s \times s$
$A =$ _____ x _____
$A =$ _____

2

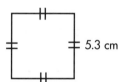
5.3 cm

$A =$ _____

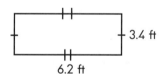
3.4 ft
6.2 ft

$A =$ _____

3 The length of a rectangle is 9 inches. If the area is 54 square inches, what is the width?

_____

4 If you double the length of each side of a square, what will happen to the area? Give an example to prove your answer.

_____

Name _____

Determining Volume

53

⭐ **Volume** is the number of cubic units needed to fill a solid object.
The formula for finding volume is
V (volume) = L (length) x W (width) x H (height).

A swimming pool is 26 feet long, 18 feet wide, and 8 feet deep. How much dirt was removed to put in the swimming pool?

This question is asking you to find the volume of the swimming pool.
To solve, multiply 26 x 18 x 8 = 3,744. Volume is measured in cubic units, so there were 3,744 cubic feet of dirt removed to put in the swimming pool. This may also be written as 3,744 ft³.

Find the volume.

1 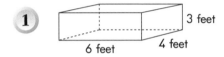 3 feet
6 feet 4 feet

_____

2 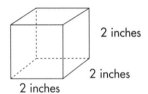 2 inches
2 inches
2 inches

_____

_____

3 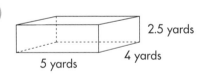 2.5 yards
5 yards 4 yards

_____

4 Joan is designing a rectangular closet for her clothes. Which of these has the most storage space? Show your work.

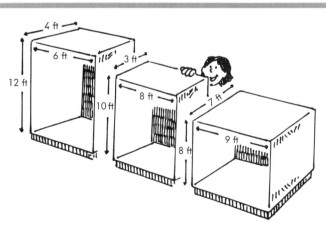

5 The volume of a box is 60 cubic feet. What are its possible dimensions? _____

Determining Circumference

54

⭐ The distance around the outside of a circle is known as its **circumference**. The **diameter** is a line segment with endpoints on the circle that goes through the center. The **radius** is a line segment that goes from the center to a point on the circle.

The diameter of a circle is twice the radius. $d = 2r$

The circumference is found by multiplying the diameter, d, by π. The value of π is 3.14. $C = \pi d$

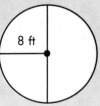

8 ft

The diameter of this circle is 2 x 8 = 16 ft.
The circumference of this circle is 3.14 x 16 = 50.24 ft.

---

1 Complete this table. Show your work.

Circumference	Radius
	5 inches
43.96 yards	
	2 feet
25.12 meters	

2 The diagram below shows the traffic circle in Westville.

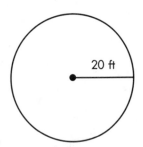

20 ft

If it is 20 feet from the center of the traffic circle to the outside, how far would a car travel if it made one complete trip around? _____

Solving Problems

55

Solve.

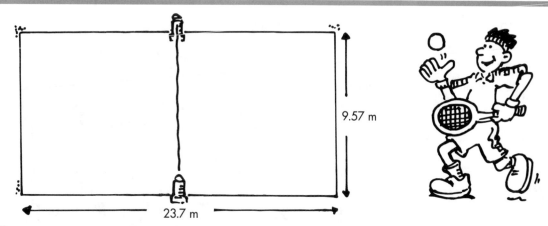

9.57 m

23.7 m

1 If you walked around the outside of the court, how far would you walk? _____

2 The court shown is for doubles, where teams of two people play against each other. For singles, where one person plays another, the court is 1.37 meters less in width than for doubles. How does the perimeter of the singles court compare to the doubles court?

_____

3 If the perimeter of the table is 853 centimeters, what is the width?

_____

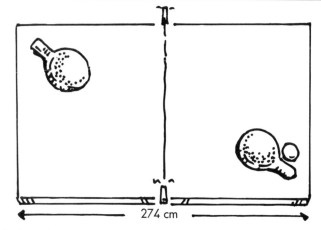

274 cm

4 If you decrease the length of the table by 5 centimeters, what would you have to do to the width to leave the perimeter unchanged? Explain your answer. _____

_____

Solving Problems

56

Solve.

Jenny was having a house built. The blueprint is shown below.

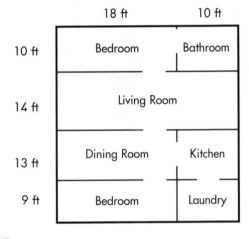

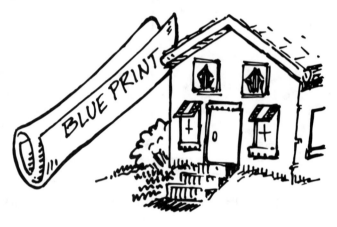

1 What is the area of the living room? _____

2 Which has a greater area, the living room or the combined area of the dining room and the kitchen? _____

3 What is the area of the house? _____

Tom needs to buy a new refrigerator. He sees an advertisement for these two models.

4 If the volume of the Super Deluxe model is 110 ft³, what is its depth? _____

5 How does the volume of the Ultraquiet model compare to the volume of the Super Deluxe model? _____

6 If Tom decided to buy the Ultraquiet model, how much floor space should he plan on using? _____

Changing Dimensions

57

Write a phrase or sentence to answer the question.

10 feet

6 feet

1 How would the perimeter of the figure above change if the width were doubled?
_____

2 How would the area of the figure above change if the length were increased by 2 feet? _____

3 If you increase by 5 feet the width of a rectangle with a perimeter of 24 feet, what has to happen to the length for the perimeter to remain unchanged? _____

4 The area of a square has changed from 16 ft^2 to 36 ft^2. How has the length of each side been changed? _____

5 How can you change the area of a figure without changing its perimeter? _____

6 The formula for the area of a triangle is ½ b (base) x h (height). For the triangle shown below, what would happen to the area if the height were increased by 2 inches? _____
_____
_____

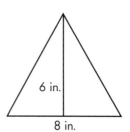

6 in.

8 in.

7 How would the perimeter be affected if the length of each side of the triangle were decreased by 1 inch?
_____
_____

Name _____

Proportional Relationships

58

★ Kelly worked on her report 2 of the last 3 days. Over the next 15 days, she will spend the same portion of her time on the report. How many days will she be working on her report? Write a proportion and solve.

$\dfrac{2}{3} = \dfrac{?}{15}$

$3 \times ? = 2 \times 15$

$? = 30/3$

$? = 10$

Kelly will work on her report 10 of the next 15 days.

Ian was looking at a map. He noticed that the scale of the map is 2 inches = 500 miles. If two cities are 6 inches apart, what is the actual distance between these cities? Write a proportion and solve.

$\dfrac{2 \text{ inches}}{500 \text{ miles}} = \dfrac{6 \text{ inches}}{x}$

$2x = 3000$

$x = 1500 \text{ miles}$

The cities are actually 1,500 miles apart.

1. There are 2 boys for every 5 girls in Mr. Brown's math class. If there are 21 students in the class, how many are boys? _____

2. Ken took 2 breaks on a 5-mile hike. How many breaks will he take if the walks 15 miles? _____

3. The scale of a map is 10 centimeters = 400 kilometers. If the distance between two points on the map is 50 centimeters, what is the actual distance between these points? _____

4. Two towns are actually 150 miles apart. On a map, they are 3 inches apart. What is the scale being used? _____

5. Two lakes are 5 inches apart on a map. The scale being used is 1 inch = 75 miles. How far apart are the lakes? _____

Advantage Math Grade 6 © 2004 Creative Teaching Press

Name _____

Scale Drawings

59

⭐ Melanie was planning a trip. How far will Melanie have to drive from her home to the lake?

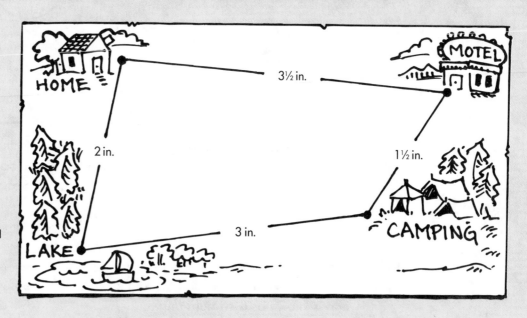

First, read the map scale, which is 1 inch = 20 miles. Next, use a ruler to measure the distance from Melanie's home to the lake. It is 2 inches. Last, write and solve a proportion.

$$\frac{1 \text{ inch}}{20 \text{ miles}} = \frac{2 \text{ inches}}{x}$$ $x = 40$ Melanie will drive 40 miles.

Solve.

1 What is the actual distance from the motel to Melanie's home? _____

2 What is the actual distance from the lake to the camping area? _____

3 There is a museum that is 90 miles from the camping area. What is the distance on the map? _____

4 If the map scale is changed to 1 inch = 10 miles, what will happen to the map distance between different points? _____

Angles

60

 Steve had to meet Bill at the library at 3:00.

Use a protractor to measure the angle formed by the hands on the clock. You will notice that the hands meet at an angle of 90°. A **right angle** is 90°.

Steve knew he had to leave his house at 2:00 to get to the library on time. Measure the angle formed by the hands on the clock.
Since the angle is less than 90°, it is classified as an **acute angle**.

Steve and Bill stayed at the library until 6:00.
The hands on the clock form a straight line. This is measured as 180° and is known as a **straight angle**.

By the time Steve arrived home it was 7:15.
The hands of the clock meet at an angle greater than 90°. This angle is classified as an **obtuse angle**.

Measure these angles. Write **obtuse, right, acute,** or **straight.**

1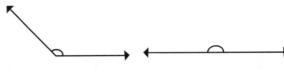

_____   _____   _____   _____

2 Use a ruler and a protractor to draw an obtuse, a right, an acute, and a straight angle. Label your angles.

Classifying Triangles

61

⭐ Triangles may be classified by the lengths of their sides.
An **equilateral triangle** has three sides of equal length.

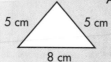

An **isosceles triangle** has two sides of the same length.

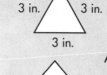

A **scalene triangle** has sides of three different lengths.

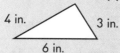

Triangles can also be classified by their angles. The three angles of a triangle always add up to 180°.
An **acute triangle** has three angles that each measure less than 90°.

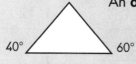

An **obtuse triangle** contains one obtuse angle that is greater than 90°.

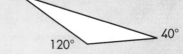

A **right triangle** contains one right angle that measures 90°.

Write **scalene, isosceles,** or **equilateral** to classify each triangle.

1

 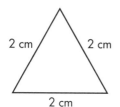

2 Write **right, acute,** or **obtuse** to classify each triangle.

 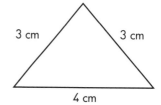 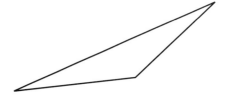

Determining the Measure of a Missing Angle

62

⭐ **Supplementary angles** are two angles whose measures add up to 180°.

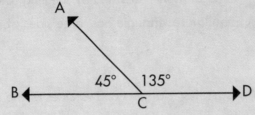

45°   135°

Angles ACB and ACD are supplementary because the sum of their measures is 180°.

Complete the tables below for these supplementary angles.

1

Angle 1	Angle 2
85°	
	43°
	100°

Angle 1	Angle 2
76°	
	120°
27°	

⭐ **Complementary angles** are two angles whose measures add up to 90°.

60°   30°

Angles QSR and RST are complementary since the sum of the measures of the angles is 90°.

Complete the tables below for these complementary angles.

2

Angle 1	Angle 2
40°	
	38°
72°	

Angle 1	Angle 2
35°	
	22°
50°	

Metric and U.S. Customary Measurement

63

Metric Length
10 millimeters = 1 centimeter
100 centimeter = 1 meter
1,000 meters = 1 kilometer

Metric Volume
1,000 milliliters = 1 liter
1,000 liters = 1 kiloliter
1 liter = 0.264 gallon

U.S. Customary Length
1 foot = 12 inches
1 yard = 3 feet
1 mile = 5,280 feet

U.S. Customary Volume
8 fluid ounces = 1 cup
2 cups = 1 pint
2 pints = 1 quart
4 cups = 1 quart
4 quarts = 1 gallon

Complete the conversions.

1 60 in. = _____ ft   27 mi. = _____ ft   830 cm = _____ m

2 88 c = _____ qt   120 oz = _____ c   220 mm = _____ cm

3 4.5 m = _____ cm   3 L = _____ gal   3.5 km = _____ m

4 The Olympic record for the 20-kilometer walk is held by Robert Korzeniowski. He completed the distance in 1 hour, 18 minutes, 59 seconds. How many meters did he walk? _____

5 Why is 50 millimeters greater than 4 centimeters? _____

6 A bottle holds 2 liters of soda. How many milliliters of soda are in the bottle? _____

7 Which is larger, a fish tank holding 3 gallons of water or a fish tank holding 2,879 milliliters of water? _____

8 Ernie bought 2 gallons of milk for the 3 children in his family. If each child drinks 32 fluid ounces of milk, will he have enough milk? _____

9 Helen bought 6 containers of juice for her party. If each container holds 64 fluid ounces, how many pints of juice does Helen have? _____

Name _____

Metric and U.S. Customary Measurement

64

 Metric Mass
1,000 milligrams = 1 gram
1,000 grams = 1 kilogram

U.S. Customary Weight
16 ounces = 1 pound
2,000 pounds = 1 ton

Complete the conversions.

1 1,500 g = _____ kg   15 g = _____ mg   4.3 kg = _____ g

2 0.5 lb = _____ oz   3,000 lbs = _____ tons   4 tons = _____ lbs

3 2,500 mg = _____ g   6 kg = _____ g   240 oz = _____ lbs

4 Jose is putting together 20 packages of cookies for a party. If he uses boxes of cookies weighing a total of 6 kilograms, how many grams of cookies will he use for each package?

_____

5 Sam wanted to buy paper for his 20 classmates. He calculated he would need a total of 3 kilograms of paper. Sam decided to buy 25 packages of paper weighing 113 grams each. Did Sam buy enough paper for his classmates? If not, how much more paper will he need to buy? Explain your answer.

_____

_____

6 Male gorillas can weigh as much as 390 pounds. If there are 6 fully grown male gorillas, about how many tons is their combined weight?

_____

7 There is a sale on bags of soil at two garden centers. At the first garden center, bags of soil are sold at $6.00 for 320 ounces. At the second garden center, the bags are sold at $4.00 for 15 pounds. Which garden center is offering the better price? Explain your answer.

_____

_____

Name _____

Exact Answers and Estimates

65

⭐ Sometimes an estimate can be used to help answer the question. Other times you may need an exact answer.

Write a sentence or two to solve and explain your answer.

1 Dave has 294 feet of fencing. He uses 16 yards of fencing to enclose his garden. If he needs 250 feet of fencing to enclose the rest of his property, does he have enough?

_____

_____

2 Jeffrey has a large box of nails weighing 2 pounds. He wants to put them in smaller boxes weighing 8 ounces each. If he has 5 smaller boxes, does he have enough boxes to hold the nails?

_____

_____

3 If a rectangular room measures 13 feet by 19 feet, would the perimeter of the room be less than 30 yards?

_____

_____

4 Wendy has 3 bags of apples weighing 1,300 grams, 1,420 grams, and 1,288 grams. If she wants to give ¼ of the apples to her friend Sophia, how many kilograms of apples will she give Sophia?

_____

_____

5 Pedro can walk 12 kilometers in 3 hours. Does he walk more than 5,000 meters per hour?

_____

_____

Name _____

66

Use estimation to solve these problems. Show your work.

1 A car weighs 2,207 pounds. Would 5 of these cars weigh more than 5 tons?

_____

2 A square mile measures 1 mile on each side. If you walked around the outside of a 1-square-mile area, would you walk more than 8,000 yards?

_____

3 A large measuring cup can hold 1 liter of liquid. Would 10 of these cups have a capacity of more than 9,800 milliliters of liquid?

_____

4 Anna measured 50 cups of water to fill her fish tank. About how many gallons does the fish tank hold?

_____

5 Harry had a giant 2⅕-meter-tall sunflower in his garden. Was the sunflower taller than 2,000 centimeters?

_____

6 Bill is cutting pieces of wood to make a picture frame that will measure 26 inches long and 13 inches wide. If he has 6 feet of wood, does Bill have enough wood to complete his project?

_____

7 Joanne is buying special tiles for her kitchen floor. She has a budget of $900 for this project. The room measures 7 yards long and 6 yards wide. The tiles are 1 foot square and sell for $1.79 each. Has Joanne budgeted enough money for this project?

_____

Take a Test Drive

Fill in the bubble beside the correct answer.

1 Which number shows the area of the larger of the two rectangles below?

○ 19.66 ft
○ 22.155 sq ft
○ 18.5 ft
○ 21.375 sq ft

3.5 feet
6.33 feet

4.75 feet
4.5 feet

2 A kilogram is equal to about 2.2 pounds. If a rock weighs 2,057 kilograms, what is its weight in pounds?

○ 935 lbs
○ 1,028.5 lbs
○ 2,079 lbs
○ 4,525.4 lbs

3 There was 323 cubic feet of cement poured for a new patio the Johnson family was putting in back of their house. If the patio was 19 feet long, how wide and deep was the patio?

○ 17 inches wide and 1 inch deep
○ 17 inches wide and 1 foot deep
○ 1 foot wide and 17 feet deep
○ 17 feet wide and 17 feet deep

4 Over the years, the size of a hamburger has increased. In 1954, the average hamburger served weighed 3.9 ounces. In 2003, the weight had increased to an average of 4.4 ounces. If you eat a hamburger once a week, about how much more would you eat in 2003 than in 1954?

○ 1 lb 10 oz
○ 12 lbs 10.8 oz
○ 14 lbs 4.8 oz
○ 16 lbs 4 oz

5 Angle A measures 49°. If Angle B is complementary to Angle A, what is the measure of Angle B?

○ 49°
○ 41°
○ 131°
○ 311°

6 Washington, D.C., and New York City are about 250 miles apart. One map was drawn using a scale of 1 inch = 50 miles. Another map used a scale of 1 inch = 25 miles. What would be the difference in the distance between the two cities on the first map compared to the second?

○ 5 inches
○ 10 inches
○ 15 miles
○ 5 miles

68

Take a Test Drive

Fill in the bubble beside the correct answer.

1. One circle has a circumference of 37.68 centimeters, while another circle's circumference is 50.24 centimeters. What is the length of the radius in each circle?
- ○ 3 cm and 4 cm
- ○ 6 cm and 8 cm
- ○ 12 cm and 16 cm
- ○ 24 cm and 32 cm

2. The volume of a fish tank is 5,400 cubic inches. What are the possible dimensions of the fish tank?
- ○ 9 in. x 20 in. x 30 in.
- ○ 9 sq in. x 20 sq in. x 30 sq in.
- ○ 90 cu in. x 30 cu in. x 6 cu in.
- ○ 45 in. x 40 in. x 30 in.

3. Ella uses 4 ounces of turkey to make a turkey sandwich. If she is making 10 sandwiches for a picnic, how much turkey will she need?
- ○ 10 lbs 4 oz
- ○ 2 lbs 8 oz
- ○ 3 lbs 4 oz
- ○ 40 lbs

4. Which number could be another angle in a right triangle, besides the right angle?
- ○ 45°
- ○ 90°
- ○ 180°
- ○ 360°

5. Which could NOT be the dimensions of a rectangle with an area of 36 square feet?
- ○ 9 ft x 4 ft
- ○ 13 ft x 2 ft
- ○ 72 ft x 0.5 ft
- ○ 36 ft x 1 ft

6. A box is 20 centimeters long, 8 centimeters wide, and 6 centimeters high. How many cubes that are 2 centimeters on each side can fit in the box?
- ○ 12
- ○ 40
- ○ 120
- ○ 400

7. If an equilateral triangle has a perimeter of 30 meters, what is the length of each of its sides?
- ○ 5 meters
- ○ 10 meters
- ○ 15 sq m
- ○ 20 cu m

8. There are 4 metric cups in 1 liter. If a container of orange juice holds 8 metric cups of juice, what is its capacity in milliliters?
- ○ 200 ml
- ○ 2,000 ml
- ○ 4,000 ml
- ○ 800 ml

Points and Lines

69

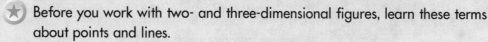

⭐ Before you work with two- and three-dimensional figures, learn these terms about points and lines.

A **point** is an exact location. Often a point is named with a capital letter. Where lines cross (**intersect**) there is a point.

A **line** is a straight path with no endpoints. Two points on the line may be used to name it.

You can say this is "line CD" or you can write $\overleftrightarrow{CD}$ or $\overleftrightarrow{DC}$.

A **ray** is part of a line that goes forever in one direction. Its end is known as its **endpoint**. It is named by saying the name of its endpoint first and then another point on the ray.

This is "ray FG." It may be written as $\overrightarrow{FG}$.

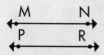

Parallel lines are always the same distance apart so they never cross. We say, "line MN is parallel to line PR."

We write $\overleftrightarrow{MN} \parallel \overleftrightarrow{PR}$.

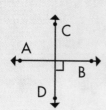

Perpendicular lines are lines that intersect to form right angles, which are 90°. We say, "line AB is perpendicular to line CD."

We write $\overleftrightarrow{AB} \perp \overleftrightarrow{CD}$.

Use the figure below for items 1 and 2.

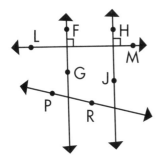

1 Name the parallel lines. _____

2 Name the 2 sets of perpendicular lines.

_____ _____

Name _____

Angles

70

⭐ Angles are formed when two rays have a common endpoint. This endpoint is known as the **vertex**.

You can say, "this is angle ABC" or you can write ∠ ABC.

Acute angles measure less than 90°. **Obtuse angles** measure greater than 90°.

Right angles measure 90°. **Straight angles** measure 180°.

Draw and name the following.

obtuse angle	acute angle
right angle	straight angle
2 parallel lines	a line segment that intersects 2 parallel lines to form 8 right angles
a line segment that intersects 2 parallel lines to form 4 obtuse angles and 4 acute angles	

Two-Dimensional Figures

71

⭐ All of us look at pictures in newspapers, books, or magazines. We say these pictures are **two-dimensional** because they are flat. They are also known as plane figures because they are drawn on a single plane. A **plane** is a flat surface.

A **polygon** is a closed plane figure whose sides are line segments. A **regular polygon** has sides that are equal length and all angles are the same. Polygons are classified by their angles and their number of sides.

Four-sided figures are classified as **quadrilaterals**. There are several quadrilaterals.

A **parallelogram** has two pairs of parallel and **congruent** (the same length) sides.

A **square** has four congruent sides that meet at right angles.

A **rectangle** has two pairs of congruent, parallel lines that form four right angles.

A **diagonal** is a line segment that joins two vertices of a polygon but is not one of the sides. In a rectangle or square, the diagonal forms two congruent triangles.

A **rhombus** is a parallelogram with four congruent sides.

A **trapezoid** has two sides that are parallel.

A **pentagon** is a five-sided polygon.

A **hexagon** is a six-sided polygon.

An **octagon** is an eight-sided polygon.

Two-Dimensional Figures

 72

Name each polygon.

1 _____

 _____

2 _____

_____

Name the quadrilateral.

3 has opposite sides congruent, right angles _____

4 has 4 congruent sides _____

5 has 4 congruent sides and 4 right angles _____

6 has 1 pair of parallel sides _____

Write a phrase or sentence to answer the question.

7 Which 3 quadrilaterals are also parallelograms? _____

8 Why can't a trapezoid be a regular polygon? _____

Symmetry

73

⭐ If a figure can be folded into two exact halves, it has a **line of symmetry**. This heart can be folded into two matching halves, so you can say it is symmetrical.

Some figures have more than one line of symmetry. This square has horizontal, vertical, and diagonal lines of symmetry.

If a figure has **point** or **rotational symmetry,** it can be rotated less than a full turn and still look exactly the same.

Answer these questions about symmetry.

1 Are the letters shown below symmetrical? If they are, draw the lines of symmetry.

C D F H I M R W X Y

2 How many lines of symmetry does this triangle have?

Circle the figure that has point symmetry.

3

    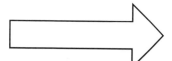

4

Name _____

Congruent and Similar Figures

74

★ **Similar figures** have the same shape but different sizes.

Congruent figures are the same shape and same size.

Answer these questions about similar and congruent figures.

1 Write **similar** or **congruent** to describe each pair of figures.

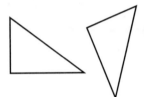

_____   _____   _____

2 Two buildings are similar. The first building is half as tall as the second building. If the shorter building is 50 feet tall, how tall is the larger building? _____

3 An equilateral triangle has a perimeter of 18 inches. Another triangle has 6-inch sides. Are these triangles congruent or similar? Explain your answer. _____
_____

4 Which statement about these octagons is NOT true? Explain your answer.

      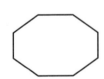

Each of the octagons has 8 vertices.
All the octagons are similar.
Two of the octagons are congruent.
All the octagons have more than one line of symmetry.

Name _____

Mixed Practice

75

Follow the directions for each item.

1 Circle the figures that show a line of symmetry.

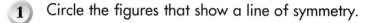

2 The human body is symmetrical. Explain why this statement is true.

_____

_____

3 Annette says that these two stop signs are congruent. Is she correct? Why?

_____

_____

_____

4 Draw two congruent quadrilaterals.

5 Alex bought a new sprinkler that sprays water in a 15-foot radius. Jerry bought a different brand of sprinkler that sprays water in a 20-foot radius. What is the circumference of the spray for each sprinkler? Write a sentence telling how Alex's sprinkler compares with Jerry's sprinkler.

_____

_____

Mixed Practice

76

Shown below is a section of a map of Southville. Use it to answer questions 1 and 2.

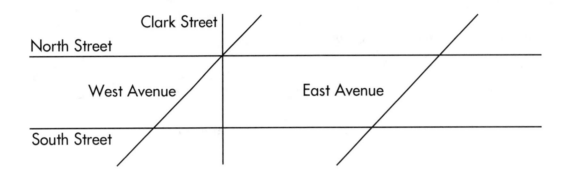

1 How would you describe the relationship between North and South Streets?

_____

_____

2 Where do the intersecting streets form an obtuse angle?

_____

3 Look at the arrangement shown below. Connect the points to make a square, a triangle, and a rectangle. Each figure must touch an even number of points. The rectangle and the triangle must touch the same number of points. The figures may not touch each other.

Coordinate Grids

77

⭐ The ordered pair (2, 2) is marked on the grid shown below. The first number in the ordered pair is the **x-coordinate**. It tells you how far to move left or right from the origin. This point is 2 units to the right of the origin. The second number is the **y-coordinate**. This point is 2 units above the origin.

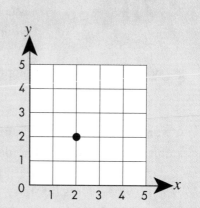

Name the ordered pair for each point on the coordinate grid.

1 Point A _____

2 Point B _____

3 Point C _____

4 Point D _____

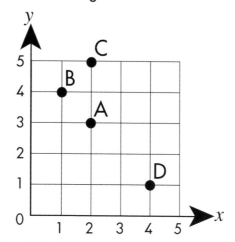

Plot the following ordered pairs on the grid.

5 Point E (1, 1)

6 Point F (1, 4)

7 Point G (3, 1)

8 Point H (3, 4)

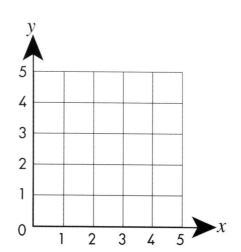

Transformations

78

⭐ When you look in a mirror, everything is reversed. You are looking at your reflection.

In geometry, **reflection** is flipping a figure over a line. It is also called a **flip**.

A **translation** is sliding a figure along a line. It is also called a **slide**. In this example, the triangle slides to the right and up.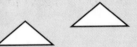

When a wheel turns it rotates. A **rotation** is the turning of a figure around a point. It is also called a **turn**.

Follow the directions for each item.

1 Does the shape or size of a figure change when you slide, flip, or rotate it? Write a sentence explaining your answer. _____

2 Write **reflection, translation,** or **rotation** to describe each set of figures,

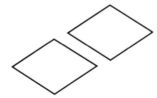 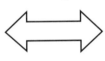

_____   _____   _____

3 Draw a picture of the figure shown below if it were reflected and then rotated.

4 There is a triangle with vertices (3, 1), (5, 1), and (4, 3). How would you describe the move of the triangle if the new vertices of the triangle are (4, 1), (6, 1), and (5, 3)?

_____

Name _____

Take a Test Drive

Fill in the bubble beside the correct answer.

Use the figure below to answer the questions.

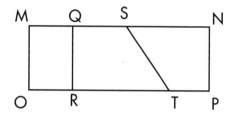

1 $\overline{MN}$ || _____

○ $\overline{NP}$ ○ $\overline{QR}$

○ $\overline{ST}$ ○ $\overline{OP}$

2 $\overline{MN}$ ⊥ _____

○ $\overline{PT}$ ○ $\overline{QR}$

○ $\overline{ST}$ ○ $\overline{OP}$

3 ∠STP = _____

○ 45°
○ 90°
○ 135°
○ 180°

4 ∠NST is _____.

○ an acute angle
○ a right angle
○ a straight angle
○ an obtuse angle

5 Which angle is NOT a right angle?

○ ∠TPN
○ ∠ORT
○ ∠PNS
○ ∠ORQ

6 Figure MSTO is a _____.

○ rectangle
○ square
○ quadrilateral
○ triangle

Name _____

Take a Test Drive

Fill in the bubble beside the correct answer.

1 How many lines of symmetry can the pentagon shown below have?

○ 0
○ 1
○ 2
○ 3

Many of the streets of Washington, D.C., are arranged in a grid. Use the grid to answer questions 5–7.

2 Which statement is true?

○ All triangles are similar.
○ All triangles are congruent.
○ All squares are congruent.
○ All squares are similar.

5 The National Gallery of Art is 4 blocks east and 3 blocks south of the FBI building. What are the coordinates of the National Gallery of Art?

○ (5, 0)
○ (6, 1)
○ (4, 3)
○ (4, 1)

3 What type of movement is shown?

○ reflection
○ translation
○ rotation
○ turn

6 The National Museum of Natural History is located at which coordinates?

○ (0, 4)
○ (4, 0)
○ (0, 0)
○ not enough information

4 Which is NOT a two-dimensional figure?

○ square
○ circle
○ line
○ rectangle

7 How does a road going east to west on the grid relate to a road going north to south?

○ parallel
○ congruent
○ perpendicular
○ similar

Patterns

81

⭐ A **function** is a connection between two numbers that form a pattern. This relationship can be shown in a **function table**.

Jay walks 3 miles each day after school. How far would Jay walk in 1 week?

Days	1	2	3	4	5
Miles	3	6	9	12	15

Jay would walk 15 miles in a week.

Complete each table.

1

2	3	4	5	6
9	11	13	15	

21	24	27	30	33
6	7	8	9	

2 The tables show a pattern between "IN" and "OUT" numbers. Complete the tables.

IN	OUT
3	9
5	15
7	21
9	
11	33

IN	OUT
5	10
8	
11	22
14	
	34

3 During a thunder and lightning storm, to estimate how far away the storm is, count the number of seconds between the time you see lightning and hear thunder. Divide that number by 5 to find the distance in miles to the storm. Write a sentence to describe the pattern that the formula is based on. Set up a table to show the time between a lightning flash and a thunderclap if the storm is 10, 20, 30, and 40 miles away.

_____

Patterns

82

Write a number, phrase, or sentence to answer the question.

1 Jeremy drew the following design. Draw the direction the tenth arrow will be facing.

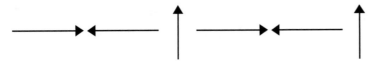

2 Draw how many dots will be in the 8th group.

3 What would be the next number in these patterns? Write the rule the pattern follows.

96, 48, 24, 12, _____   _____

2, 7, 6, 11, 10, _____   _____

1, 2, 3, 6, 7, 14, _____   _____

20, 18, 19, 17, 18, _____   _____

4, 13, 40, 121, _____   _____

4 Study the pattern below. What digit will be in the ones place in 2^{11}? _____

$2^1 = 2$
$2^2 = 4$
$2^3 = 8$
$2^4 = 16$
$2^5 = 32$
$2^6 = 64$

Variables

83

⭐ A basketball team scored 5 more points in the first half than the second half of a game. How many points did they score in the first half? If we use the letter b to represent the second half points, then the expression $b + 5$ represents the first half points.

If the team scored 40 points in the second half, they scored $40 + 5 = 45$ points in the first half.

A **variable** is a letter used to represent one or more numbers.

$b + 5$ is an **expression**. An expression contains at least one operation ($+$, $-$, $\div$, or x) and sometimes a variable.

Evaluate these expressions if $f = 8$, $g = 4$, and $h = 2$.

1 $h + 7 =$ _____ $10g =$ _____ $f \div 2 =$ _____

Evaluate the expression $5d$ for each value of d.

2 $d = 8$ $d = 4$ $d = \frac{1}{2}$

     $5d =$ ____ $5d =$ ____ $5d =$ ____

3 The area of Rhode Island is represented by the expression $606d$. What is the area of Rhode Island if $d = 2$ square miles?

_____

4 In 1950, rain forests covered about 16% of the earth's land. By 2000, the amount of rain forest could be represented by the expression $16\% - r$. What percent of the earth's land was covered by rain forests in 2000 if $r = 9\%$?

_____

5 Most of the air we breathe is composed of nitrogen. The percentage may be represented by the expression $100n$. What percentage of the earth's atmosphere is composed of nitrogen if $n = 0.781$?

_____

Algebraic Expressions

84

Write an expression with a variable for each situation described below. Then write a phrase telling what the variable represents.

1 Jason had 12 cookies and then ate some. _$12 - x$ x = the cookies Jason ate_

2 Loretta had 5 books and then bought some more. _____

3 Hal had 8 pens. He bought 5 more and then gave away some. _____

Write an expression, then evaluate the expression.

4 Barbara saved d dollars a week from her job for 6 weeks. How much did Barbara save? Evaluate the expression for d = $18.75. _____

5 Tom had $40 before he went shopping. After he bought some school supplies, he had n left. How much did Tom spend on school supplies? Evaluate the expression for n = $15. _____

6 Complete the table. Write an expression or a sentence.

	nine more than d
$g + 20$	
	three less than p
$z \div 3$	
	six times as much as k
$(w \times 6) + 3$	

7 The dimensions of Kate's yard are three times the dimensions of Phillip's yard. Write an expression that compares the area of Kate's yard to the area of Phillip's yard.

_____

Name _____

Graphing Functions

85

⭐ Each car traveling in the HOV (High Occupancy Vehicle) lane of a highway must have at least 2 passengers during morning and evening rush hours. If each car averages 2 passengers, the relation between cars and passengers can be shown in the table below.

Number of Passengers (p)	2	4	6	8	10
Number of Cars (c)	1	2	3	4	5

The relationship between the number of cars and passengers is shown in the equation $p = 2c$.
In the graph, values of c are plotted along the x-axis and values of p are plotted along the y-axis.

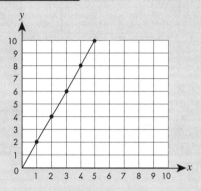

Create a table and graph for each situation.

1 Bernadette is training for a race. She began running 1 mile the first day. The next day she ran 1 mile more than the day before. This pattern continued for the next 5 days.

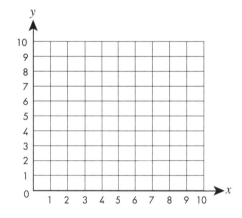

2 If you love being near the water, Florida may be the place for you. For every 8 square miles of land, there is about 1 square mile of water.

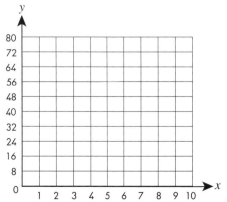

Graphing Functions

86

⭐ What two numbers from 1–10 have a product of 16 and a sum of 10?

$a \times b = 16$

a	1	2	4	8	16
b	16	8	4	2	1

$a + b = 10$

a	1	2	3	4	5
b	9	8	7	6	5

1 Graph both sets of ordered pairs on the same grid. Where do the lines intersect? This is the solution to the problem.

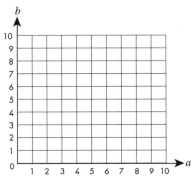

2 Create a table based on the information in this graph. Write a sentence about the relationship between the number of nights and the number of pages Jane read.

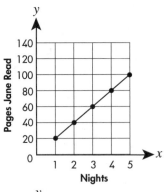

3 Create a table based on the information in this graph. Write a sentence about the relationship between the number of hours and the number of customers in a clothing store.

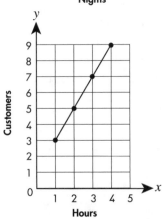

Equations

87

⭐ An **equation** is a mathematical sentence that shows that two quantities are equal.

The Los Angeles Dodgers have won 54 games. The New York Mets have won 11 games fewer than the Dodgers. How many games have the Mets won?

$m = 54 - 11$
$m = 43$

The New York Mets have won 43 games.

Solve.

1 Jack wants to buy a television. He already has $80.75 in his bank account. After saving for a month, he has $143.89. Write the equation that may be used to find how much Jack saved during the month. Explain your answer.

_____

_____

2 There are about 8 million tons of copper produced each year. There is about half as much lead produced as copper and 2 million tons more of zinc produced than lead. Write an equation to find how much lead and zinc is produced each year. Explain your answer.

_____

_____

3 Phil sent a letter with some photos to his grandmother. The post office charged 37 cents for the first ounce and 20 cents for each additional ounce. If the letter cost 77 cents to mail, how much did it weigh? Write an equation to solve this problem and explain your answer.

_____

_____

4 The 6th grade is going on a trip to the zoo. They are taking 3 buses and 38 students can fit on each bus. If the number of students going on the trip is represented by the equation, $n = (38 \times 2) + 12$, how many sixth graders went on the trip? Show your work and explain your answer.

_____

_____

Inequalities

88

 An **inequality** is a mathematical sentence that compares two unequal expressions.

The Pittsburgh Pirates have fewer than 47 victories. How can you represent this statement?

$v < 47$

Unlike an equation, an inequality may have more than one solution. Any number less than 47 would be the solution to this inequality.

Solve.

1 Which number can be used to make both number sentences true? _____
$5 \times m = 20$ $5 + m > 8$

2 If $10 < y > 8$, what is the value of y? _____

3 Explain why $5\frac{1}{2}$ and $3\frac{3}{4}$ are solutions of $x < 6$.

_____

4 There is an unimaginable number of stars in the night sky. Because of this, astronomers divide the sky into more than 80 sections. This way, they can pinpoint the location of any star. This is known as the star's address. The number of sections is represented by the inequality $80 < s < 90$. What are the possible solutions to this problem? Explain your answer.

_____

_____

5 Each of the planets has a different number of moons. Complete the table to show how many moons each planet has.

Mercury	$m < 1$	_____
Venus	$m < 1$	_____
Earth	1	_____
Mars	$1 < m < 3$	_____
Jupiter	$15 < m < 17$	_____
Saturn	18	_____
Uranus	$14 < m < 16$	_____
Neptune	$7 < m < 9$	_____
Pluto	$0 < m < 2$	_____

Analyzing Data

89

The pictograph below shows the number of items for sale in the school store. Use it to answer questions 1 and 2.

Item	Number							
Packages of Pens	x	x	x	x	x	x	x	⟩
Packages of Markers	x	x	x	x	x	x	x	x
Notebooks	x	x	x	x	x			
Book Bags	x	x	x	⟩				

KEY: **x** = 20 items

1 How many more notebooks were for sale than book bags? _____

2 If all the packages of pens are sold at a cost of $0.99 each, how much will the school store make? _____

This stem-and-leaf plot shows the number of visitors to a museum in each of 8 hours on Tuesday.

Stem	Leaves
3	2 7
4	1 2 5 8 9
5	4

You can see there were 32, 37, 41, 42, 45, 48, 49, and 54 visitors to the museum. You can also see the range (difference between high and low) of data is 22 (54 − 32).

This stem-and-leaf plot shows the scores of the top 10 finishers in a golf tournament. Use it to answer questions 3, 4, and 5.

Stem	Leaves
27	1 1 3 5 7 9
28	1 2 4 6

3 Which score occurs most often? _____

4 What is the range of golf scores? _____

5 If the eleventh place finisher had 288, how would this be shown on the stem-and-leaf plot? _____

Creating Graphs

90

⭐ Twelve students recorded how much television they watched last week. Their results are shown on the line plot below.

Hours of Television Watched

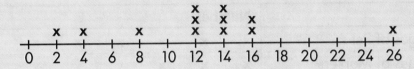

A **line plot** shows the spread of data. Most of the students watched between 12 and 16 hours of television. 26 hours is known as the **outlier**, since it is separated from the rest of the data.

Look at the table shown. Create a line plot. Use it to answer questions 1 through 3.

State	Population (millions)
Georgia	7
Indiana	6
Louisiana	5
Minnesota	5
New Jersey	8
Pennsylvania	13
Washington	6
Wisconsin	5

1 Do most states have more or less than 5 million people? Explain your answer.

_____

2 Which state's population was the outlier?

_____

3 What is the combined population of New Jersey and Louisiana?

_____

Interpreting Graphs

91

The double-line graph below shows the average monthly temperatures for the cities of Dallas and San Antonio in Texas. Use this graph to answer the questions that follow.

Month	Dallas	San Antonio
January	54	50
February	60	52
March	68	58
April	76	68
May	83	71
June	91	78
July	95	87
August	95	80
September	88	75
October	78	65
November	65	60
December	56	50

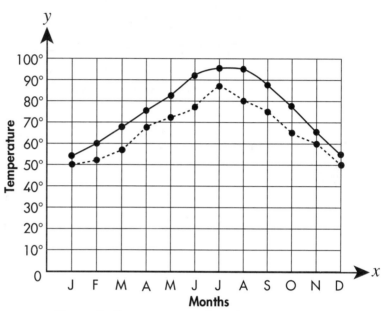

Key: Dallas = —— San Antonio = ------

1 In which month do the cities have the least difference in temperature when compared to each other?

_____

2 Between which two months does Dallas have the least change in temperature?

_____

3 Which city would you rather visit in the summer? Explain your answer.

_____

4 How do you know you'll probably need to wear a coat in San Antonio more often than in Dallas?

_____

Organizing Data

92

⭐ The **range** is the difference between the highest and lowest numbers.

The **median** is the number in the middle when the numbers are placed in order.

The **mode** is the number that appears most often. There can be more than one mode, and sometimes there is no mode.

The **mean** is also known as the **average**. To find the mean, you first add all the numbers. Then divide the sum by the number of addends.

1 Find the range, median, mode, and mean of this set of data. Show your work.

range _____

median _____

mode _____

mean _____

Trail	Length
Jeremy's Run	14.0 miles
Bluff Trail	13.0 miles
Cedar Run	7.7 miles
Rocky Mount	9.8 miles
Doyles River	6.5 miles
Pine Hill Gap	5.9 miles
Turk Branch	20.8 miles

2 If you were just finding the mean, why wouldn't you have to arrange the numbers in order?

_____

_____

Some minerals are harder than others. A scale has been developed which is known as the Mohs Scale of Mineral Hardness. The lower the number, the more easily a mineral can be scratched. For instance, quartz is 7 on the scale, calcite 3, diamond 10, talc 1, and fluorite 4.

3 What are the range, median, mode, and mean of this set of data?

range _____ median _____ mode _____ mean _____

4 Can the mode and the median be the same number? Why?

_____

_____

Name _____

Tree Diagrams and Organized Lists

93

⭐ Jake is getting dressed for school. He can choose a white, blue, or red shirt. He has black, gray, blue, and tan pants. How many outfits does Jake have? You can make an organized list to solve this problem.

White Shirt	**Blue Shirt**	**Red Shirt**
black pants	black pants	black pants
gray pants	gray pants	gray pants
blue pants	blue pants	blue pants
tan pants	tan pants	tan pants

You can also make a tree diagram.

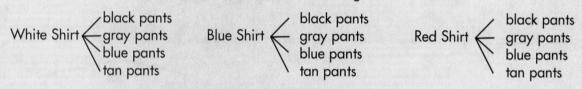

Jake can choose from 12 possible outfits.

You can also use the **counting principle** to find the number of outfits. Multiply the different types of pants by the different types of shirts: 4 x 3 = 12 choices.

Make an organized list, draw a tree diagram, and use the counting principle to find your answer.

1. The kitchen store is having a sale on pots. They come in 1, 2, 3, and 3.5 quart sizes. You can choose from pots made from aluminum or cast iron. How many different choices do you have?

Probability

94

⭐ **Probability** is the chance of an event occurring. An event is the outcome you're looking for. Sean is using the spinner shown. If he spins it 40 times, what are the chances that he'll spin a 3?

In this example, 3 is the event or the **favorable outcome**. When you use the spinner, there are 8 **possible outcomes:** 1, 2, 3, 4, 5, 6, 7, and 8.

You find probability by: $\dfrac{\text{favorable outcomes (1)}}{\text{number of possible outcomes (8)}}$

If you spin the spinner once, there is a ⅛ chance you will spin a 3.
To find the probability of the spinner landing on 3 if you use the spinner 40 times: multiply ⅛ x 40 = 5. The spinner should land on 3 five times.

---

1 You are rolling a six-sided number cube and the sides are numbered 1–6. If you roll the number cube 30 times, how many times will you roll an even number?

_____

2 If you roll two number cubes 36 times, how many times will you roll a sum of 6?

_____

3 If you reach in the bag shown above, are you more likely to pull out a marble marked 1 or a marble marked 3? _____

4 What is the probability you will pull out a marble that is NOT marked 1 or 2?

_____

5 What is the probability you will pull out an even-numbered marble? _____

Name _____

Take a Test Drive

Fill in the bubble beside the correct answer.

---

1 Jack bought 2 books for $13.95 each and a magazine for $3.95. If he paid with a $50 bill, which number sentence can be used to find his change?

- ○ $50 − $13.95 + $3.95 = x
- ○ $50 − ($13.95 + $3.95) = x
- ○ $50 − ($13.95 + $13.95 + $3.95) = x
- ○ $50 + ($13.95 + $13.95 + $3.95) = x

Use the table below to answer questions 4–5. Starting with Christopher Columbus in 1492, many explorers sailed from Europe to the "New World." The table below shows some explorers and their dates of exploration.

Explorer	Date
Giovanni Cabato	1497
Pedro Alvarez Cabral	1499<?<1501
Ferdinand Magellan	1519–1522
Francisco Pizzaro	?
Juan Rodriquez Cabrillo	1542

---

2 What value of x will NOT make both number sentences true?

$20 − x > 10$
$20 \div x < 10$

- ○ 1
- ○ 4
- ○ 5
- ○ 6

4 During which year did Cabral sail?

- ○ 1497
- ○ 1500
- ○ 1520
- ○ 1542

---

3 Trevor worked 6 hours a day for 4 days. If he was paid $8 per hour, and he saved ¼ of his earnings, how much did he save? Which equation correctly solves this problem?

- ○ (6 × 4) × (8 × 4) = x
- ○ (6 + 4 + 8) ÷ 4 = x
- ○ (6 × 4 × $8) ÷ 4 = x
- ○ (6 × 4) × ($8 ÷ 4) = x

5 Pizzaro claimed the Inca Empire, along the South American west coast, as part of Spain. Pizzaro's starting date is shown by the equation e = 1492 + 39. Its ending date is shown by the expression e + 4. When did Pizzaro's trip begin and when did it end?

- ○ 1453–1449
- ○ 1453–1457
- ○ 1531–1535
- ○ 1527–1531

Name _____

Take a Test Drive

Fill in the bubble beside the correct answer.

---

1 If 45 − x = 30, what is x?
- ○ 9
- ○ 6
- ○ 10
- ○ 15

2 Dave is three times as old as Jane. Jane is 4 years younger than Amy. Amy is 6 years old. How old is Dave?
- ○ 5
- ○ 6
- ○ 13
- ○ 30

3 The Eiffel Tower in France is 984 feet tall. The CN Tower in Canada is 820 feet taller than the Eiffel Tower. Which equation correctly shows the height of the CN Tower?
- ○ 984 − 820 = 164 feet
- ○ 984 + 820 = 1,704 feet
- ○ 984 + 820 = 1,804 feet
- ○ 984 x 820 = 806,880 feet

4 A shirt costs $25.00. If the sales tax is 6%, which expression tells the total cost?
- ○ $25.00 ÷ 0.06 = $1.50
- ○ $25.00 x 0.06 = $1.50
- ○ $25.00 − ($25.00 ÷ 0.06) = $23.50
- ○ $25.00 + ($25.00 x 0.06) = $26.50

5 Jeff had 6 apples. He bought 4 more and shared the apples with his 2 brothers. Which expression shows the number of apples each brother received?
- ○ (6 − 4) ÷ 3 = ⅔ apple
- ○ (6 + 4) ÷ 3 = 3⅓ apples
- ○ (6 + 4) ÷ 2 = 5 apples
- ○ (6 − 4) ÷ 2 = 1 apple

6 Molly had $47.95 when she left her house to go to the museum. While she was there, she paid an admission fee, ate lunch, and bought some postcards. When she got home, she had $7.50 in her pocket. How much did she spend at the museum?
- ○ $47.00
- ○ $40.45
- ○ $47.55
- ○ $48.35

Practice Test

97

Fill in the bubble beside the correct answer.

---

1 Which is NOT equal to 389,014?
- ○ 300,000 + 89,000 + 14
- ○ 3 hundred thousands + 8 ten thousands + 9 thousands + 1 ten + 4 ones
- ○ 30,000 + 8,000 + 900 + 10 + 4
- ○ three hundred eighty-nine thousand fourteen

2 In 1850, the population of St. Louis was about 70% of the population of Cincinnati. If the population of Cincinnati was about 115,000, what was the population of St. Louis?
- ○ about 50,000
- ○ about 60,000
- ○ about 70,000
- ○ about 80,000

3 There was a math test on Tuesday. Which of the following students received the highest score?
- ○ Steve
- ○ Mary
- ○ Kyle
- ○ Tina

Student	Correct
Steve	65%
Mary	0.58
Kyle	⅗
Tina	0.7

4 $12\frac{5}{8} + 1\frac{1}{2} =$
- ○ $13\frac{3}{4}$
- ○ $13\frac{6}{10}$
- ○ $14\frac{1}{8}$
- ○ $14\frac{1}{2}$

5 $\$77.85 \div 3 =$
- ○ $25.65
- ○ $26.00
- ○ $25.95
- ○ $25.75

6 If a lantern fish is 300 feet below the surface, and a mackerel is 230 feet above the lantern fish, what depth is the mackerel swimming at?
- ○ 530 feet
- ○ 70 feet
- ○ 270 feet
- ○ 90 feet

7 The expression 3^3 can be read as _____.
- ○ 9
- ○ 27
- ○ 12
- ○ 81

Name _____

Practice Test

98

Fill in the bubble beside the correct answer.

---

1 The drama club sold 75 tickets to their play. If they collected a total of $637.50, what was the price of each ticket?
- ○ $8.50
- ○ $8.75
- ○ $8.25
- ○ $7.50

2 The Atlantic Ocean measures 5,500 miles from east to west. It measures 9,000 miles from north to south. If you were drawing a map using a scale of 1 in. = 500 mi, what would the dimensions be?
- ○ 10 in. x 19 in.
- ○ 12 in. x 16 in.
- ○ 11 in. x 18 in.
- ○ 13 in. x 16 in.

3 Charles had 8½ yards of rope to tie up some bundles of books. If each bundle requires 1½ yards of rope, how many bundles can Charles tie up?
- ○ 3
- ○ 4
- ○ 5
- ○ 6

4 Alaska has an area of about 570,000 square miles. Which of the following choices represents this area using the correct prime factorization?
- ○ $57 \times 2^4 \times 5^4$
- ○ $57 \times 4 \times 2^2 \times 25 \times 5^3$
- ○ $57 \times 2 \times 4 \times 5 \times 4$
- ○ $57^4 \times 2 \times 5^4$

5 The least common multiple of 4, 6, and 8 is _____.
- ○ 12
- ○ 16
- ○ 20
- ○ 24

6 The greatest common factor of 16 and 24 is _____.
- ○ 2
- ○ 4
- ○ 6
- ○ 8

7 A rectangle has an area of 24 square feet. What dimensions would yield the greatest perimeter?
- ○ 24 feet x 1 foot
- ○ 6 feet x 4 feet
- ○ 12 feet x 2 feet
- ○ 8 feet x 3 feet

8 A car was driven at an average speed of 56.71 miles per hour. On the next trip, its average speed was 2.85 miles per hour less. What was the car's average speed on the second trip?
- ○ 59.56 mph
- ○ 53.86 mph
- ○ 54.46 mph
- ○ 57.16 mph

Practice Test

99

Fill in the bubble beside the correct answer.

---

1 Which statement is NOT true?

- ○ A right triangle is also scalene.
- ○ All angles in an equilateral triangle measure 90°.
- ○ There are two equal angles in an isosceles triangle.
- ○ An obtuse triangle contains one angle larger than 90°.

2 A grain silo has a radius of 15 feet. What is its circumference?

- ○ about 47 feet
- ○ about 94 feet
- ○ about 706 feet
- ○ about 508 feet

3 A storage box has a volume of 192 cubic feet. If its length is 8 feet and its width is 4 feet, what is the height of the storage box?

- ○ 4 feet
- ○ 5 feet
- ○ 6 feet
- ○ 7 feet

4 There are two complementary angles. If one angle measures 35°, the other angle measures _____.

- ○ 55°
- ○ 145°
- ○ 10°
- ○ 45°

5 Joe wants to build a garden with an area of 80 square feet. He has 36 feet of fencing to surround the rectangular garden. What dimensions should his garden have?

- ○ 9 feet by 4 feet
- ○ 10 feet by 8 feet
- ○ 12 feet by 3 feet
- ○ 12 feet by 6 feet

6 Many earthquakes happen at the shallow depth of 18 miles. How many yards below the earth's surface do the earthquakes occur?

- ○ 31,680 yards
- ○ 95,040 yards
- ○ 648 yards
- ○ 18,000 yards

7 Which of the following sets of figures shows a reflection?

8 298 x 3.28 =

- ○ 38.74
- ○ 977.44
- ○ 3874
- ○ 97,744

Name _____

Fill in the bubble beside the correct answer.

1 What is the probability of both a six-sided number cube landing with an odd number showing and a coin landing face up?

○ 1 in 2
○ 1 in 8
○ 1 in 4
○ 1 in 6

2 Which three-dimensional figure has no faces and 2 bases?

○ a cube
○ a triangular prism
○ a sphere
○ a cylinder

3 What is the next figure in the pattern shown below?

4 Jared drew a tree diagram with 20 branches to represent his choices in sports clubs he could join at different locations. He could find the same answer by multiplying _____.

○ 12 x 8   ○ 18 x 2
○ 5 x 4   ○ 6 x 3

Use the table for questions 5 and 6.

Name	Born	Died
John Adams	1735	1826
Frederick Douglass	1817	1895
Pocahontas	1595	1617
Theodore Roosevelt	1858	1919

5 How long did Pocahontas live?

○ 22 years
○ 32 years
○ 66 years
○ 78 years

6 When is the mean birth date for these people?

○ 1735
○ 1751
○ 1776
○ 1814

Math Grade 6 Tracking Sheet

Activity	Possible	My Score
Unit 1		
1	9	
2	9	
3	1	
4	12	
5	6	
6	18	
7	8	
8	15	
Test Scores		
9	8	
10	8	
Unit 2		
11	13	
12	17	
13	17	
14	18	
15	11	
16	11	
17	18	
18	19	
19	8	
20	13	
21	22	
22	17	
23	22	
24	17	
25	14	
26	15	
27	24	

Activity	Possible	My Score
28	26	
29	19	
30	18	
31	7	
32	6	
33	7	
34	7	
35	10	
36	11	
37	11	
38	6	
Test Scores		
39	8	
40	7	
Unit 3		
41	4	
42	4	
43	8	
44	8	
45	13	
46	7	
47	6	
48	41	
Test Scores		
49	8	
50	8	
Unit 4		
51	7	
52	6	
53	5	

Activity	Possible	My Score
54	5	
55	4	
56	6	
57	7	
58	5	
59	5	
60	8	
61	6	
62	12	
63	15	
64	13	
65	5	
66	7	
Test Scores		
67	6	
68	8	
Unit 5		
69	2	
70	7	
72	10	
73	4	
74	6	
75	5	
76	3	
77	8	
78	6	
Test Scores		
79	6	
80	7	
Unit 6		

Activity	Possible	My Score
81	7	
82	8	
83	9	
84	11	
85	2	
86	3	
87	4	
88	13	
89	5	
90	3	
91	4	
92	4	
93	1	
94	5	
Test Scores		
95	5	
96	6	
97	7	
98	8	
99	8	
100	6	

Math 6 Answer Key

Activity 1
1. five million, ninety-three thousand, one hundred eighty-five
2. seven million, four hundred thirty-one thousand, fifty
3. four million, eight hundred thirty thousand, four
4. twenty-three thousandths
5. three and fifty-nine hundredths
6. two and six hundred seven thousandths
7. four and three-eighths
8. two and one-sixth
9. twelve-thirteenths

Activity 2
1. $(2 \times 1,000,000) + (3 \times 100,000) + (5 \times 1,000) + (4 \times 100) + (6 \times 10) + (7 \times 1)$
2. $(1 \times 10) + (4 \times 0.1) + (9 \times 0.01)$
3. $(5 \times 1,000) + (4 \times 100) + (1 \times 10) + (3 \times 1) + (2 \times 0.1)$
4. $(5 \times 0.01) + (4 \times 0.001)$
5. 7,085,629
6. 4,708.4
7. 8,050.09
8. 0.047
9. 0.268

Activity 3
1. $\frac{1}{5} = \frac{2}{10}$ $\frac{3}{10} > \frac{2}{10}$
   The log weighs more because $\frac{3}{10}$ is greater than $\frac{1}{5}$.

Activity 4
1. 2.098, 2.908, 2.980, 3.089
2. 0.013, 0.031, 0.103, 0.301
3. 0.187, 0.781, 0.817, 0.871
4. $\frac{3}{5} > \frac{4}{7}$ $\frac{4}{9} > \frac{3}{8}$ $\frac{2}{3} < \frac{3}{4}$
5. 84%   63%   92%
6. 55%   99%   100%

Activity 5
1. 0.5
2. $\frac{4}{5}$
3. $\frac{4}{5}$
4. 0.08
5. 0.5, $\frac{1}{2}$
6. Monday

Activity 6
1. 0.2 $\frac{1}{5}$
2. 60%   0.6 $\frac{3}{5}$
3. Other Countries - 5%
   Eastern Europe - 20%
   Northwestern Europe - 20%
   Southern Europe - 25%
   Central Europe - 30%
4. 70%   0.7 $\frac{7}{10}$

5.

Decimal	Fraction	Percent
0.60	$\frac{3}{5}$	**60%**
0.24	$\frac{6}{25}$	**24%**
0.8	$\frac{4}{5}$	80%
0.06	$\frac{3}{50}$	**6%**
0.3	$\frac{3}{10}$	**30%**
0.55	$\frac{11}{20}$	55%

Activity 7
1. 3×2^3 $3 \times 2 \times 5$
   5×2^3
2. 1,000   25   16
3. $2^5 \times 5^3$
4. 84

Activity 8
1. 192   48   135
2. 96   738   1,696
3. 41   16
4. 56   22.5
5. 3   6
   16   10.4
6. 15 miles

Activity 9–Take a Test Drive
1. $\frac{3}{5}$
2. 81
3. 24%
4. 2,067,801
5. 0.75
6. 0.078
7. $\frac{11}{20}$
8. 0.080

Activity 10–Take a Test Drive
1. 4
2. fifty-six thousandths
3. 4
4. 4%
5. $3 \times 3 \times 5$
6. 0.21
7. 6.560   6.506   6.056
8. $\frac{7}{20}$

Activity 11
1. 157,159   4,295,495
   54,112,082   1,244,765
   18,888
2. 6,041,744   50,739
   6,975   9,337,739
   111,785
3. 103,212
4. Jeff didn't carry the one into the thousands place. 80,397.
5. 183,609

Activity 12
1. 5,331,637   1,554,888
   48,546   558,146
   8,017,021
2. 11,268,539   6,946,944
   29,274   8,642,525
   79,801
3.

$$\begin{array}{rrr} 2,965 & 47,203 & 1,862,393 \\ -1,576 & -36,385 & -10,472 \\ \hline 1,389 & 10,818 & 1,851,921 \end{array}$$

$$\begin{array}{rr} 8,229,214 & 83,650 \\ -572,129 & -3,209 \\ \hline 7,657,085 & 80,441 \end{array}$$

4. 3,583 feet
5. There is a greater difference between Cho Oyu and Nanga Parbat (1,119 feet).

Activity 13
1. 6.6   41.05   9.413
   127.32   28.38
2. 12.528   44.65   456.4
   389.84   69.726
3. 588.025   115.157
   1,138.87   19,290.096
   15,652,183.469
4. 281.21
5. Yes, the combined average of Candie Kung and Karrie Webb is higher by 1.47 strokes.

Activity 14
1. 1.38   2.08   40.65
   460.89   502.159
2. 3.591   38.423   3,603.011
   0.588   76,942.94
3. 51.045   3.78   5,854,391
   472,803.25   34,083.95
4. 1.85°F
5. $22
6. 0.263 square mile

Activity 15
1. $\frac{8}{15}$ $5\frac{5}{8}$ $1\frac{1}{6}$
2. $5\frac{17}{21}$ $1\frac{7}{12}$ 1
3. $8\frac{9}{20}$ $\frac{2}{3}$ $12\frac{11}{20}$
4. $2\frac{11}{30}$ $14\frac{89}{120}$

Activity 16
1. $1\frac{2}{3}$ $\frac{2}{15}$ $4\frac{11}{20}$
2. $3\frac{1}{4}$ $5\frac{2}{3}$ $\frac{5}{16}$
3. $\frac{37}{72}$ $5\frac{5}{6}$ $\frac{5}{39}$
4. $1\frac{1}{2}$ lbs
5. 5 minutes

Activity 17
1. 4   ⁻12   7   ⁻24
2. ⁻3   ⁻4   ⁻15   ⁻6
3. 5   ⁻42.4   730   ⁻10
4. ⁻10   ⁻28   134   ⁻110
5. 2°
6. $500 + ⁻$80 + $90 = $510

Activity 18
1. 3   ⁻17   ⁻11   ⁻38
2. ⁻21   ⁻11   25   ⁻13
3. ⁻36   50   93   ⁻10
4. ⁻3   40   15   ⁻90
5. 10.1°
6. 108.5°F
7. 400 feet

Activity 19
1. $2\frac{13}{24}$ feet
2. $2\frac{3}{8}$ feet
3. $\frac{3}{8}$ inch
4. $5\frac{5}{8}$ feet
5. 2,743,924 square kilometers
6. 179,864,494 people
7. 8,488,999 square kilometers
8. 25,509,297 people

Activity 20
1. 37 floors
2. 27 floors
3. 29 floors
4. $4\frac{11}{24}$ 5,740,331
5. $1\frac{3}{5}$ 3,889
6. 41   899,639
7. >
8. >
9. >
10. <

Activity 21
1. 14,256   354,754
    3,849,488   9,897,856
    38,553
2. 90,535   51,123,436
    87,400   776,400
    16,830
3. 5,750   4,032
    24,345   6,308
    522,598
4. 5,976   11,781
    255,407   6,100
    44,000

5. $3,948
6. Buying would cost $20,975 and leasing would cost $17,928, so buying would cost more.

Activity 22
1. 65R55   885   63R40
    1,074R74   768R5
2. 32R23   295R37
    760R15   306R6
    1,312R46
3. 196R5   1,035R4
    208R34   510R27   701
4. 170 kilometers per hour
5. $472,491.11

Activity 23
1. 5,434.816   5,742.5
    3,640.62   500.3165
    241.9177
2. 665.4072   51,102
    469.176   51,940
    593.296
3. 273.6   283.75
    3.48   608.344
    27.642
4. 27.5   37.704
    1,393.92   168   3.91
5. 442 times
6. 116.2 runs

Activity 24
1. 20.31   235.3   5.6
    2.2   4
2. 16.7   63.63   1,905.5
    99.86   32
3. 1.235   5.2   62.4
    1.115   32.624
4. 13 posts
5. 9 cups

Activity 25
1. $\frac{2}{3}$ 12 $\frac{1}{14}$
2. $1\frac{13}{27}$ $18\frac{19}{24}$ $\frac{16}{21}$
3. $4\frac{2}{3}$ $91\frac{2}{3}$ $\frac{7}{20}$
4. 45 $\frac{11}{12}$ $1\frac{1}{9}$
5. 1 cup
6. Ted. He walked 6 miles, compared to Brenda's 5 miles.

Activity 26
1. 4   20 $\frac{7}{8}$
2. $\frac{16}{27}$ 21 $1\frac{4}{5}$
3. $4\frac{2}{5}$ $1\frac{41}{49}$ $\frac{25}{63}$
4. $11\frac{1}{5}$ $3\frac{1}{2}$ $\frac{5}{8}$
5. 9 breaks
6. 16 hours and 40 minutes
7. 22 cents

Activity 27
1. ⁻120   8,001   32
    270   ⁻9,299
2. 222,632   ⁻1,254   18,147
    1,360   ⁻1,651
3. ⁻20,000   ⁻196   3,825
    ⁻810   1,900
4. ⁻56   correct   correct   correct
5. ⁻36   correct   correct   correct
6. $1,000

Activity 28
1. 7   ⁻7   ⁻7   ⁻32
2. 5   ⁻30   ⁻11   10
3. ⁻7   ⁻14   25   ⁻10
4. ⁻10   32   ⁻16   ⁻35
5. correct   ⁻4   correct   28
6. 7   correct   ⁻16   ⁻7
7. 5 times
8. 4 pounds

Activity 29
1. 3,936.1   152,092   547R15
    8R10.06
2. $\frac{4}{75}$ $5\frac{23}{32}$ $\frac{1}{8}$
3. 5,750   24,345   522,598
4. ⁻184   306   ⁻5,146   23   ⁻9
5. 45 feet
6. 1,636.1 miles
7. 121.3 miles
8. 798 miles

Activity 30
1. 975   ⁻0.945   12
    2,004,170
2. $\frac{1}{4}$ 8 $4\frac{4}{5}$
3. $1\frac{31}{45}$ $5\frac{2}{5}$ $11\frac{1}{21}$
4. ⁻12   14
    ⁻8,676   8,175
5. $8\frac{1}{4}$ hours
6. $37\frac{1}{2}$ minutes
7. 21°F
8. 8 friends

Activity 31
1. 6,120 meters
2. 0°C
3. 349 meters
4. 180 meters
5. 1,999,998 people
6. 3,911 people
7. 51.0972 people per square mile

Activity 32
1. 105 million kilometers
2. 225 million kilometers
3. $1\frac{1}{4}$ inches
4. 60 tons
5. 345 meters

6. 1,843.75 meters

Activity 33
1. 3,262 yards
2. 94 yards
3. 34
4. 6
5. ¾ cup
6. ¾ cup
7. 2 cups

Activity 34
1. 1,035.5 kilometers
2. 46 kilometers per hour
3. 104.0175 miles
4. 196.56 kilometers
5. 67%
6. 148.5 centimeters or 4 feet 11¼ inches
7. 10 pounds

Activity 35
1. 61
2. 5
3. 30
4. 16
5. 9
6. 60
7. 36
8. 17
9. 39
10. 39

Activity 36
1. 33
2. 201
3. 275
4. >
5. <
6. <
7. <
8. $(6 + 5) \times (9 - 2) = 77$
9. $7^2 + 8 + (6 \div 3) = 59$
10. $8 \times 6 - 4 = 44$
11. 4

Activity 37
1. 24.4/No
   28.7/Yes
   29.8/Yes
   25.7/No
   28.2/Yes
2. 5,130,000 (3)
   4,300,000 (2)
   12,400,000 (6)
   5,600,000 (4)
   3,400,000 (1)
   5,900,000 (5)

Activity 38
1. He added instead of subtracting.
   $3^4 - 11 = 70$
2. 2,000 cheetahs
3. 50,000 cheetahs
   12-pointed star = 3
   4-pointed star = 8
   wavy box = 9

Activity 39–Take a Test Drive
1. $2.7 \times {}^-2.8$
2. 4,648
3. 10
4. 3
5. 1,387,824
6. 854
7. 3,399.6
8. 462

Activity 40–Take a Test Drive
1. 6,400
2. about 686 feet per second
3. $50,000,000
4. 9⅜
5. about 4,170 meters
6. about 4,100 feet
7. 3,367 hours

Activity 41
1. Yes, it is reasonable. Round 183 miles to 200 miles and multiply by 6. That comes to 1,200 miles, which is reasonably close to 1,098 miles.
2. No, it is not reasonable. Round 3,021 calories to 3,000 calories and 21 days to 20 days. Multiply 3,000 calories by 20 days to get 60,000 calories. That is far from 6,340 calories.
3. Yes, it is reasonable. Round 17 days to 20 days and multiply that by 2,000 planes to get 40,000 takeoffs and landings. That is reasonably close to 37,111 take-offs and landings.
4. Yes, it is reasonable. Round 31 hours to 30 hours, $16.99 to $17.00, and $12.50 to $13. Multiply 30 by 12 (360) and then subtract $30 ($17 + $13) to get $330. That is reasonably close to $340.

Activity 42
1. Estimate to find that yes, the tailor has enough material. Round 5¾ yards to 6 yards and multiply by 3 to get 18, which is less than 20.

It is not necessary to use exact numbers, because the goal is to see if the tailor simply has "enough" fabric on hand.
2. You must exactly add the home run totals to find that the 85 home runs hit by the Mariners is more than the 67 home runs by the Orioles. You must be exact because you are comparing precise totals.
3. Estimate to determine that the precipitation is about 6½ inches above normal.
4. Exactly add the amount spent to determine that Alexandra should receive $2.09 in change.

Activity 43
1. composite
   1, 3, 7, 21
2. prime
   1, 41
3. composite
   1, 2, 5, 10, 25, 50
4. composite
   1, 5, 25
5. composite
   1, 2, 3, 4, 6, 8, 12, 16, 24, 48
6. 23, 29
7. 56, 81
8. because all other even numbers are divisible by 2

Activity 44
1. 1, 2, 4, 5, 8, 10, 20, 40
2. 1, 2, 3, 6, 9, 18
3. 1, 2, 4, 7, 14, 28
4. 1, 2, 4, 7, 8, 14, 28, 56
5. GCF: 6
   24: 1, 2, 3, 4, 6, 8, 12, 24
   30: 1, 2, 3, 5, 6, 10, 15, 30
6. GCF: 18
   36: 1, 2, 3, 4, 6, 9, 12, 18, 36
   54: 1, 2, 3, 6, 9, 18, 27, 54
7. GCF: 8
   16: 1, 2, 4, 8, 16
   56: 1, 2, 4, 7, 8, 14, 28, 56
8. GCF: 20
   40: 1, 2, 4, 5, 8, 10, 20, 40
   60: 1, 2, 3, 4, 5, 6, 10, 12, 15, 20, 30, 60

Activity 45
1. 24   14
2. 120   308
3. 60   16
4. 18   24
5. 40   72
6. 8

7. three packages of hamburgers and four packages of buns
8. 2, 3, 5, 7, 11, 13, 17, 19, 23, 29, 31, 37, 41, 43, 47, 53, 59, 61, 67, 71, 73, 79, 83, 89, 97

Activity 46
1. $2 \times 2 \times 2 \times 3$ $3 \times 3 \times 2 \times 2$
2. $5 \times 2 \times 2$ 7×7
3. 2×107
4. 77 (prime factors are 7 & 11)
5. Yes, because 27 is itself a factor of 54.

Activity 47
1. 2, 3, 4, 6
2. 3, 9
3. 2, 4, 5, 10
4. 2, 4
5. The elevation must be 7,964 feet, since only even numbers are divisible by 2.
6. The elevation must be 11,403, since only that number's sum is divisible by both 3 and 9.

Activity 48
1.

Number	4,650	3,820	1,638	5,124	8,145
Divisible by 2	yes	yes	yes	yes	no
Divisible by 3	yes	no	yes	yes	yes
Divisible by 4	no	yes	no	yes	no
Divisible by 5	yes	yes	no	no	yes
Divisible by 6	yes	no	yes	yes	no
Divisible by 9	no	no	yes	no	yes
Divisible by 10	yes	yes	no	no	no

2. false
3. false
4. false
5. true
6. 48
7. 87,546

Activity 49–Take a Test Drive
1. 2, 5, 8, 10, 20, 40
2. 2, 5, 3
3. 17 and 23
4. 21, 24, 27
5. 4 and 9
6. 18 and 30
7. 5
8. 603

Activity 50–Take a Test Drive
1. 2, 4, 6, 8
2. 50,000
3. 79 and 97
4. (5, 7)
5. 300,000
6. 323
7. 5, 8, and 10
8. 42 and 84

Activity 51
1. 24 feet
2. 24 centimeters
3. 14 meters
4. 52 feet
5. 10 feet by 15 feet
6. 2 feet
7. 8 yards

Activity 52
1. $A = 8$ yards $\times$ 6 yards
   48 square yards
   $A = 12$ inches $\times$ 12 inches
   144 square inches
2. 28.09 square centimeters
   21.08 square feet
3. 6 inches
4. The area will quadruple. If a square increases by 2 inches a side to 4 inches a side, its area increases from 4 square inches to 16 square inches. If a square increases from 3 inches a side to 6 inches a side, its area increases from 9 square inches to 36 square inches.

Activity 53
1. 72 cubic feet
2. 8 cubic inches
3. 50 cubic yards
4. The first closet has 288 cubic feet of storage space, the second closet has 240 cubic feet of storage space, and the third has 504 cubic feet of storage space, so the third is the largest.
5. Its possible dimensions could be any of the following:
   2 feet by 5 feet by 6 feet
   2 feet by 3 feet by 10 feet
   6 feet by 10 feet by 1 foot
   4 feet by 5 feet by 3 feet
   15 feet by 2 feet by 2 feet

Activity 54
1.

Circumference	Radius
31.4 inches	5 inches
43.96 yards	**7 yards**
12.56 feet	2 feet
25.12 meters	**4 meters**

2. 125.6 feet

Activity 55
1. 66.54 meters
2. The double's court perimeter is 63.8 meters, which means it is shorter than the single's court perimeter by 2.74 meters.
3. 152.5 centimeters

4. You would have to increase the width by the same amount, 5 centimeters.

Activity 56
1. 392 square feet
2. The living room has the greater area.
3. 1,288 square feet
4. 4 feet
5. The Super Deluxe is 38 cubic feet larger.
6. 12 square feet

Activity 57
1. The perimeter would increase by 12 feet.
2. The area would increase by 12 square feet.
3. The length would have to decrease by 5 feet.
4. The length of each side increased by 2 feet (from 4 feet to 6 feet).
5. You can change the area of a figure without changing the perimeter by lengthening one side by the same amount that you shorten another side.
6. The area of the triangle would increase by 8 square inches.
7. The perimeter would decrease by 3 inches.

Activity 58
1. 6 boys
2. 6 breaks
3. 2,000 kilometers
4. 1 inch = 50 miles
5. 375 miles

Activity 59
1. 70 miles
2. 60 miles
3. $4\frac{1}{2}$ inches
4. The distance would double.

Activity 60
1. acute   right
   obtuse   straight
2. acute: (Angles may vary.)

   right:

   obtuse: (Angles may vary.)

   straight:

Activity 61
1. equilateral   scalene   isosceles
2. right   acute   obtuse

Activity 62
1.

Angle 1	Angle 2
85°	95°
137°	43°
80°	100°

Angle 1	Angle 2
76°	104°
60°	120°
27°	153°

2.

Angle 1	Angle 2
40°	50°
52°	38°
72°	18°

Angle 1	Angle 2
35°	55°
68°	22°
50°	40°

Activity 63
1. 5   142,560   8.3
2. 22   15   22
3. 450   0.792   3,500
4. 20,000 meters
5. 50 millimeters is the same as 5 centimeters, which is greater than 4 centimeters.
6. 2,000 milliliters
7. 3 gallons
8. Yes. Two gallons equals 256 ounces, more than 3 x 32 ounces, or 96 ounces.
9. 24 pints

Activity 64
1. 1.5   15,000   4,300
2. 8   1½   8,000
3. 2.5   6,000   15
4. Jose will use 300 grams for each package.
5. No, Sam did not buy enough. He has 2,825 grams, but he needs 3,000 grams (or 3 kilograms). So Sam needs 2 more packages to get at least 3,000 grams.
6. 1 ton
7. The 320-ounce bag for $6 would be $18 for 60 pounds. The 15-pound bag for $4 would be $16 for 60 pounds, so the $4 15-pound bag is a better deal.

Activity 65
1. No, he'll be 4 feet short. He'll use 48 feet for the garden, leaving only 246 feet left.
2. Yes, he needs only four boxes.
3. Yes, the perimeter would be only 64 feet, or 21 yards and 1 foot.
4. Wendy will give 1 kilogram to Sophia.
5. No, Pedro runs at 4 kilometers (4,000 meters) per hour.

Activity 66
1. Yes (Five cars would weigh more than 11,000 pounds .5 tons = 10,000 pounds.)
2. No (1 mile is 1,760 yards, so 4 miles would be less than 8,000 yards.)
3. Yes (1 liter is 1,000 milliliters, so 10 cups of 1 liter each would hold 10,000 milliliters, which is more than 9,800 milliliters.)
4. About 3 gallons
5. No (2⅕ meters is 220 centimeters, which is less than 2,500 centimeters.)
6. No (Bill needs two 26-inch pieces and two 13-inch pieces, which adds up to 78 inches, more than the 72 inches that 6 feet of wood would provide.)
7. Yes (Joanne's kitchen is 21 feet x 18 feet, so she needs 378 1-foot-square tiles. At $1.79 each, the total cost of the tiles is $676.62, less than her $900 budget.)

Activity 67–Take a Test Drive
1. 22.155 sq ft
2. 935 lbs
3. 1 foot wide and 17 feet deep
4. 1 lb 10 oz
5. 41°
6. 5 inches

Activity 68–Take a Test Drive
1. 6 cm and 8 cm
2. 9 in. by 20 in. by 30 in.
3. 2 lbs 8 oz
4. 45°
5. 13 ft by 2 ft
6. 120
7. 10 meters
8. 2,000 ml

Activity 69
1. $\overleftrightarrow{FG} \parallel \overleftrightarrow{HJ}$
2. $\overleftrightarrow{FG} \perp \overleftrightarrow{LM}$ $\overleftrightarrow{HJ} \perp \overleftrightarrow{LM}$

Activity 70
obtuse angle: (Angles may vary.)

acute angle: (Angles may vary.)

right angle:

straight angle:

2 parallel lines:

a line segment that intersects 2 parallel lines to form 8 right angles:

a line segment that intersects 2 parallel lines to form 4 obtuse angles and 4 acute angles:

Activity 72
1. octagon   rectangle
2. triangle   pentagon
3. rectangle
4. rhombus
5. square
6. trapezoid
7. square, rectangle, and rhombus
8. A trapezoid can't be a regular polygon because all of the sides of a trapezoid can't be the same. At least one side must be longer than the other sides.

Activity 73
1. C D H I M W X Y
2. 1

3. (the rectangle should be circled)
4. (the octagon should be circled)

Activity 74
1. congruent   similar   congruent
2. 100 feet
3. congruent
   For an equilateral triangle to have a perimeter of 18 inches, it must have 6-inch sides, giving it the same shape and size as the second triangle.
4. "All the octagons are similar" is not true. The two "stretched" octagons are not similar to the other two octagons.

Activity 75
1. (the circle and the diamond should be circled)
2. The human body is symmetrical because the left side and right side look alike.
3. No. The stop signs are oriented the same and of the same shape, but one is simply smaller. They are similar.

4. (Drawings will vary.)

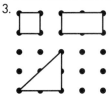

5. Alex's sprinkler spray has a circumference of 94.2 feet. Jerry's sprinkler spray has a circumference of 125.6 feet. Alex's sprinkler spray circumference is 31.4 feet less than Jerry's sprinkler spray circumference.

Activity 76
1. North and South Streets are parallel.
2. South Street and West Avenue
   South Street and East Avenue
   North Street and West Avenue
   North Street and East Avenue
3.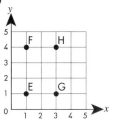

Activity 77
1. (2, 3)
2. (1, 4)
3. (2, 5)
4. (4, 1)
5. – 8.

y-axis shown with points F and H at y=4 (x=1 and x=3), E and G at y=1 (x=1 and x=3)

Activity 78
1. No, it simply re-orients the object.
2. translation   reflection
   rotation
3. reflected:

   rotated:

4. translation

Activity 79–Take a Test Drive
1. $\overline{OP}$
2. $\overline{QR}$
3. 135°
4. an acute angle
5. ∠ORT
6. quadrilateral

Activity 80–Take a Test Drive
1. 1

2. All squares are similar.
3. translation
4. line
5. (5, 0)
6. not enough information
7. perpendicular

Activity 81
1.

2	3	4	5	6
9	11	13	15	**17**

21	24	27	30	33
6	7	8	9	**10**

2.

IN	OUT
3	9
5	15
7	21
9	**27**
11	33

IN	OUT
5	10
8	**16**
11	22
14	**28**
17	34

3. (Time between lightning and thunder) ÷ 5 = Miles to storm

Miles away	Time between lightning and thunder
10	50 seconds
20	1 minute 40 seconds
30	2 minutes 30 seconds
40	3 minutes 20 seconds

Activity 82
1. ⟶
2. 48 dots
3. 6; each number is half of the number before it
   15; alternate adding five and subtracting 1
   15; alternate doubling the number and adding 1
   16; alternate subtracting two and adding 1
   364; add 3 raised by an exponent that grows by 1 each time
4. 8

Activity 83
1. 9   40   4
2. 40   20   2.5
3. 1,212 square miles
4. 7%
5. 78.1%

Activity 84
1. 12 – x   x = the cookies Jason ate
2. 5 + x
   x = additional books Loretta bought
3. 8 + 5 – x, or 13 – x
   x = pens Hal gave away
4. $112.50
5. $25

6.

d + 9	nine more than d
g + 20	**20 more than g**
p – 3	three less than p
z ÷ 3	**a third of z**
6 x k	six times as much as k
(w x 6) + 3	**3 more than six times as much as w**

7. K = area of Kate's yard
   P = area of Phillip's yard
   K = 3 x P

Activity 85
1.

Day (x)	1	2	3	4	5
Miles (y)	1	2	3	4	5

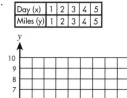

2.

Sq. mi. of land (y)	8	16	24	32	40	48	56	64
Sq. mi. of water (x)	1	2	3	4	5	6	7	8

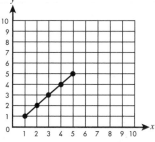

Activity 86
1. 2, 8

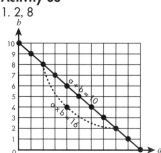

2. Each night Jane reads 20 pages.

1	2	3	4	5
20	40	60	80	100

3. There is one more than twice as many customers in the store as the number of hours the store has been open.

1	2	3	4
3	5	7	9

Activity 87
1. $x = \$143.99 - \$80.75$, where $x =$ how much Jack saved during the month.
2. Use the variables c for copper, l for lead, and z for zinc.
   $c = 8,000,000$ tons
   $l = \frac{1}{2}c$
   $l = 4,000,000$ tons
   $z = l + 2,000,000$ tons
   $z = 6,000,000$ tons
3. 3 ounces
   $w =$ weight in ounces, $p =$ postage
   $p = 37¢ + [20¢ \times (w - 1)]$
   This equation says the letter costs 37¢ plus 20¢ for each ounce, minus the first ounce.
4. 88. $n = (38 \times 2) + 12 = 88$

Activity 88
1. 4
2. any number greater than 11
3. Both $5\frac{1}{2}$ and $3\frac{3}{4}$ are solutions because both are less than 6.
4. Any number greater than 80 but less than 90.
5.

Mercury	$m < 1$	0
Venus	$m < 1$	0
Earth	1	1
Mars	$1 < m < 3$	2
Jupiter	$15 < m < 17$	16
Saturn	18	18
Uranus	$14 < m < 16$	15
Neptune	$7 < m < 9$	8
Pluto	$0 < m < 2$	1

Activity 89
1. 30
2. $148.50
3. 271
4. 15
5. $28\overline{\smash{)}8}$

Activity 90

1. More
2. Pennsylvania
3. 13 million

Activity 91
1. January
2. July to August
3. Answers may vary, but they should note that Dallas is hotter in summer and San Antonio is cooler in summer.
4. You'll likely need to wear a coat in San Antonio more often than in Dallas because San Antonio's lowest average temperatures are lower than the lowest average temperatures in Dallas.

Activity 92
1. range: 14.9 miles
   median: 9.8 miles
   mode: none
   mean: 11.1 miles
2. You don't have to arrange the numbers in order to find the mean because all you need to do is add them and divide by the number of addends.
3. range: 9
   median: 4
   mode: none
   mean: 5
4. Yes, if the median also happens to be the number that appears most often.

Activity 93
1.

Aluminum	Cast Iron
1 quart	1 quart
2 quarts	2 quarts
3 quarts	3 quarts
3.5 quarts	3.5 quarts

$4 \times 2 =$

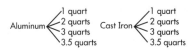

Activity 94
1. 15
2. 5
3. 3
4. $\frac{8}{15}$
5. $\frac{7}{15}$

Activity 95—Take a Test Drive
1. $\$50 - (\$13.95 + \$13.95 + \$3.95) = x$
2. 1
3. $(6 \times 4) \times (\$8 \div 4) = x$
4. 1500
5. 1531–1535

Activity 96—Take a Test Drive
1. 15
2. 6
3. $984 + 820 = 1,804$ feet
4. $\$25.00 + (\$25.00 \times 0.06) = \$26.50$
5. $(6 + 4) \div 3 = 3\frac{1}{3}$ apples
6. $40.45

Activity 97—Practice Test
1. $30,000 + 8,000 + 900 + 10 + 4$
2. about 80,000
3. Tina
4. $14\frac{1}{8}$
5. $25.95
6. 70 feet
7. 27

Activity 98—Practice Test
1. $8.50
2. 11 in. x 18 in.
3. 5
4. $57 \times 2^4 \times 5^4$
5. 24
6. 8
7. 24 feet x 1 foot
8. 53.86 mph

Activity 99—Practice Test
1. All angles in an equilateral triangle measure 90°.
2. about 94 feet
3. 6 feet
4. 55°
5. 10 feet by 8 feet
6. 31,680 yards
7. ⇨ ⇦
8. 977.44

Activity 100—Practice Test
1. 1 in 2
2. a cylinder
3. ⬠
4. 5×4
5. 22 years
6. 1751